Praise For Health ~~~~~ *Of Life*

"This book is the most comprehensive health book I've ever read. It's so practical it's mind-blowing. I'm afraid this singular book could singlehandedly get rid of 70% of the health issues people face in their life—if they'll follow the instructions therein. I have always believed in divine health, but the reality has been a painful and sad one for most Christians who get sick and also die from sicknesses and illnesses. It was like a dilemma to believe in something and not know how to actualize it. This book from Dr. Garwood resolves this dilemma at long last. The missing link has been a lack of comprehensive kingdom knowledge in regards to health. Now I can truly say that the gospel of the kingdom is indeed the total answer for man's total need. The word of God is undoubtedly the absolute answer to man's absolute needs, even in regards to health. Thank you so much Dr. Garwood for giving this gift to the world. It will surely outlive you."

Dr. Sunday Adelaja
Pastor of Embassy of God, Kiev, Ukraine
Author of *Church Shift*

"In our years of health research and activism, we have long hoped that leaders in the church would stand up and be a voice for truth in the realm of health and wellness. In his seminal, one-of-a-kind book *Health for All of Life*, Dr. Jason Garwood has answered that prayer. We can't recommend it enough."

Ty and Charlene Bollinger
Founders of *The Truth About Cancer*
and *The Truth About Vaccines*

"Rev. Dr. Jason Garwood has done a fantastic job exposing society's almost cult-like following of modern medicine. I pray that his careful, Biblical approach of explanation will help open the eyes of many believers to both the benefits of, and responsibility to, care for one's body and lead one's family to do the same using as many of the natural tools God has already provided.

Honestly, I've been so discouraged by the church's willingness to ignore facts about aborted fetal tissue used as a base for many of the current vaccinations, it's adherence to state mandates that violate Biblical principles, and its dependence on a medical system that is borderline idolatry. Pastor Jason clarifies the Biblical truth that God created us as His masterpiece with the abilities to heal that contemporary science has yet to understand."

Dr. Kevin Conners
Practitioner at Conners Clinic
Author of *Stop Fighting Cancer and Start Treating the Cause*

"John Wesley knew that wisdom is required to live so as to love God with all one's strength. So he sought and compiled all the available wisdom for healthy living. In 1747 he published "Primitive Physic or an Easy and Natural Method of Curing Most Diseases." Specialists deserve respect, but the doctrine of the "Priesthood of all believers" makes everyone responsible for personal and public health. Health For All of Life will equip the reader to fulfill this responsibility in our day."

Vishal Mangalwadi
www.RevelationMovement.com
www.TruthMatters.tv

"Every Christian should find Health for All of Life to be remarkably helpful in their God-given responsibility of caring for their health—a basic and important aspect of self government.

Health for All of Life provides insight into the basic principles of health and natural medicine, as well as help to provide a foundation for a theology of health, regrettably a concept that most Christians are unfamiliar with.

God in the Proverbs has admonished us to be wise and diligent in all things. As it pertains to physical health, Health for All of Life will be of great assistance to every person who is willing to be diligent.

As we preserve and endeavor to improve our health, we can enjoy a greater sense of wellness, a sense of victory or salvation from certain aspects of disease, and life more abundant. Even more so, we can be more effective in His Kingdom and live more to the glory of God."

Rhett Bergeron, MD
Medical Director
Real Health Medical, Atlanta, GA

"Any coward can speak out against the unpopular evil of their day. The courageous and truly godly individual is marked, rather by challenging the wickedness that is embraced by the culture of their particular era. By taking on the widely accepted medical monopoly along with its messiah complex, Dr. Garwood's *Health For All of Life* distinguishes the author as a courageous Christian visionary."

Ron Kronz
Pastor & Activist
Street Church, Springfield, VA
Business Owner, Missionary with *Bishop of Souls*

"Dr. Garwood has the mind of a scholar, and the heart of a pastor, and we see the best of both callings in this book. He wants to change your mind. He's that guy who believes that truth really is liberating. He's also the pastor who gives a darn whether you personally are doing okay. If you are sick, you are unavailable for most good deeds and kingdom work. To that end, he has produced a guidebook that I predict will become a standard resource for many years to come. It uniquely marries the theoretical to the practical. Let no one put them asunder. Get the knowledge. Know the truth. Escape the Medical Industrial Complex. Take advantage of all the dynamic Action Steps. Change your life. Advance the Kingdom."

Pastor Gordan Runyan
Immanuel Baptist Church, Tucumcari, NM
Author of *Resistance to Tyrants*

"*Health for All of Life: A Medical Manifesto of Hope and Healing for the Nations* is what we need amid health crises in our nation and the world. It is a physical and spiritual return to the Biblical foundation of Christ Jesus. This book reveals that all areas of the Christian life, including health, are Gospel issues and are in need of the regeneration only Christ can bring."

Pastor Russell Traweek
Christ Covenant Church, Sweeny, TX

"For too long Christians have lived bifurcated lives, separating the sacred and the "secular." Dr. Jason Garwood brings us back to integrity and directs us in how we can manifest the reign of Christ over all things, body and soul. Informative, integrative and interesting, *Health For All of Life* honors the Lord and giver of Life and serves well His servants."

Dr. RC Sproul Jr.
Author & Teacher
Host of the *Jesus Changes Everything* Podcast

"For the better part of 30 years I have been identifying and deconstructing theological paradigms. Today, the world of physical health is also and virtually controlled by paradigms—what it is, how it's lost, restored and maintained. Yet physical health is explicitly a gospel issue since souls always come in bodies. Sadly, however, these paradigm are largely driven by half truths posing as whole truths, and many of us are unable to sort through them. In this timely, one of a kind, work Dr. Jason Garwood challenges these false paradigms and offers natural correctives in pursuit of a *Health for All of Life*."

Dr. John Noe
Author, President of Prophecy Reformation Institute
www.prophecyrefi.org

"From its inception this book was endorsed by Providence. I don't know who else could have authored it, frankly. Dr. Garwood draws from his biblical worldview, his own family's journey in search of health and healing, his inquisitive, scholarly background, and deep compassion for those who suffer. He successfully took an online natural medical resource center and wrapped it in Jesus' gospel of the kingdom. This should be a standard resource for every pastor and person of influence interested in ministering to the whole person."

Bill Evans
Kingdom Driven, LLC.
The Truck Driver Theologian
Creator of HealthForAllofLife.com

"The Scriptures repeatedly exhort us to exercise stewardship over every aspect of our lives—not the least of which includes our physical health. Our bodies are temples of the Holy Spirit after all; we are not our own; we have been bought with a price. In this helpful volume you will find a compendium of prudent and practical counsel, to the end that you and I might take appropriate steps toward an exercise of that essential stewardship. Read. Think. Pray. Live."

Pastor George Grant
Parish Presbyterian Church,
Franklin, TN

"*Health For All of Life* is Dr. Jason Garwood's powerfully provocative missile advocating, theologically and practically, for liberty in health care responsibility. It belongs to mature people or those, like me, who desire to grow into godly maturity in this area of life. Perhaps his greatest contribution herein is not his promotion of health care liberty but his exposition and advocacy of the only presupposition upon which that liberty can exist: personal responsibility and self-government consciously honoring to the Lordship of Jesus Christ, the governor of the nations. "Whether you eat or drink . . . do all to the glory of God" is taken seriously by Dr. Garwood and he more than suggests that you and I should do the same.

Make no mistake, Dr. Garwood is selling health care decisional responsibility: consciously and intentionally. He is unapologetically promoting freedom-based health care decision making embraced in the family circle. In the dominating shadows of the medical tyrannies and health care coercions of our day, this advocacy is life-giving to both health care professionals as well as families because they are freed to their respective jurisdictions and appropriate authority - neither has to "be as god." Dr. Garwood's candle will start fires providing significant contributions to the growing light of Coram Deo."

Tim Yarbrough
Reformed Elder, Business Owner
Serial Entrepreneur, Passionate Mentor to the Next Generations

HEALTH
for all of
LIFE

A Medical Manifesto of Hope and Healing
For The Nations

HEALTH
for all of
LIFE

A Medical Manifesto of Hope and Healing
For The Nations

Rev. Dr. Jason M. Garwood

B.S., M.Div., Th.D.

Cross & Crown Books
Warrentron, VA

Health for All of Life
A Medical Manifesto of Hope and Healing for the Nations

Copyright 2020 © Jason M. Garwood

Publisher:
Cross & Crown Books
41 West Lee Highway
Suite 59 Box #199
Warrenton, VA 20186

Cover Design: Red Bag Media

Scripture taken from the Modern English Version. Copyright © 2014 by Military Bible Association. Used by permission. All rights reserved.

Disclaimer. The author of this book does not dispense medical advice or prescribe the use of any technique as a form of treatment for physical, emotional, or medical problems without the advice of a physician, either directly, or indirectly. The intent of the author is only to offer information and spiritual well-being. In the event you use any of the information in this book for yourself, the author and the publisher assume no responsibility for your actions.

Printed in the United States of America.

ISBN-13: 978-1-7341228-3-1

TABLE OF CONTENTS

DEDICATION:

*To Jack and Bill for refusing to
allow ignorance of these truths to go unchallenged.*

FOREWORD
BY MARTIN G. SELBREDE

Rare is the book that is able to bridge the conceptual gap between spiritual health and medical health without compromising on one or the other element. When an author starts out by "seeking first the kingdom of God and His righteousness" (Matt. 6:33) and commits to living "by every word that proceedeth out of the mouth of God" (Matt. 4:4), he'll not stray far. Such consecration of effort invites the reader to join the author in striving to think God's thoughts after Him.

Dr. Jason Garwood is serious about the proposition that "all things cohere in Christ," inviting his readers to reclaim aspects of their lives that have long since defaulted to cultural norms in conflict both with God's Word and His creative wisdom. How often have we seen the term "Christian self-government" being paid little more than lip service? Dr. Garwood puts legs on the concept in an area where it has the most intimate impact on our own lives: our health. He extends the scope of self-government under God to embrace the whole man in all his complexity and glorious responsibility as an image-bearer of the most High.

Is it possible for this volume to be both a theology book *and* a primer on personal health? It is not only possible, it is necessary that a book like this appear in print. Our theologies are too often detached from reality, and our ideas of health are predominantly informed by humanistic impulses that exclude the Creator from providing insights into His Own creation. We treat these concerns like oil and water that cannot be mixed, let alone safely[1] united. A realignment is called for: a realignment of health according to biblically-informed parameters, and a realignment of theology to speak His Word into every realm, the medical field included. We need a faith that goes deep *and* goes wide. Dr. Garwood understands this and acts upon it.

One key take-away is Dr. Garwood's call to decentralize health and medical concerns. This doesn't require an institutional, top-down strategy: it can *and should* be achieved by individuals committed to the kingdom of God and their service to the King as they take back responsibility for their health and that of their families. It's humanism that requires conformity to a one-size-fits-all medical paradigm. By contrast, there is liberty within the Christian worldview. Under humanism, "you can keep your doctor" only until that promise is voided. When *health for all of life* is embraced, you learn to be your own doctor.

The Road to Wholistic Health

Whether you spell it holistic or wholistic, one fact stands out: one of the more obvious avenues by which people adopt wholistic health practices is when Western medicine fails them. When you're told you only have six more months to live and the doctors have nothing left to offer, motivation to look beyond your circle of practitioners kicks in with a vengeance. Patients either capitulate to the apparent death sentence or they start to do their own research beyond the bounds of Western medical practice. In other words, it

---

1   It is commonly thought that each side would lose something in the exchange: biblical faith will erode and fade into mystical irrationalism supporting scientifically untenable ideas, or will spawn countless Pharisees condemning one another for their medical decision-making. On the other hand, humanistic medicine derides all attempts for orthodox Christian theology to speak to its theory and practice, affirming instead its explicit trust in man. "Cursed is the man who trusts in man, who makes flesh his arm" (Jer. 17:5).

seems to take a crisis for humans to break out of the circle of medical convention.

Many of these individuals do better on their own than medical science would have allowed for. They either live longer than predicted (by margins that can embarrass the prophets in white coats) or go into remission (regarded as a fluke and too often dismissed as a statistical outlier by their former doctors).

The real mystery is why so many regard wholistic medicine as a last resort, rather than an excellent starting place. Why not reverse the roles and use wholistic medicine as our basic strategy and call the medical doctor as a last resort? Given that prevention dominates the wholistic paradigm, why do we not act as if we truly believe that an ounce of prevention is worth a pound of cure? How did we end up in this situation?

Dr. Garwood lays out the historical steps that have led up to the de facto monopoly now being exercised by Western medicine and its reductionist[2] view of the human body and its allopathic[3] approach to pathology. The resulting tunnel vision parallels the well-known truism that when you only have a hammer, every problem looks like a nail.

Synonyms for allopathic medicine include mainstream medicine, conventional medicine, and orthodox medicine. Note how useful these definitions are for maintaining a monopoly: the respective alternatives to these terms would be fringe medicine, uncon-

---

2   Reductionist means that the systems of the body are reduced to individual mechanical, or chemical, or electrical parts where the sum of the parts isn't greater than the whole. Analysis (cutting things into smaller pieces to study them) is important but one must not forget that the thing you're studying has been cut into pieces. The reductionist usually looks for a natural, mechanistic explanation for things without reference to a Creator while discarding any consideration of spiritual dimensions as nonexistent, or if existent, irrelevant.

3   A term now regarded as controversial: western medicine approves of labeling competing models, but dislikes it when its own paradigm is labeled. Allopathy refers to treating a medical condition with elements that oppose that pathology, e.g., providing a laxative for constipation, aspirin for fever, escalating to more severe tactics to oppose a condition, such as radiation focused on a tumor to kill It or surgery to remove it.

ventional medicine, and unorthodox medicine. These are clearly pejorative terms that instill fear, uncertainty, and doubt – and if we let others do our thinking for us, that is precisely where we will land. The language is manipulated so as to manipulate us. We're disinclined to consider alternatives, let alone looking into how elitism has crept into the mix.

It is clear that Dr. Garwood is his own man. You will soon see that he doesn't blindly follow every point made by the authorities he cites favorably. He exercises self-government with respect to them, and he invites the reader to do the same with the points that he himself is making. He doesn't call for decentralization with one hand and then hypocritically impose a new top-down orthodoxy with the other. He rather surveys the widening field of discussion and illustrates areas for his readers to start their own journey to health for all of life. This is not a force-fit agenda being promoted: this is Christian self-government geared toward maximizing our service to the King and His kingdom in every realm, especially the medical/health realm.

The author of this book goes out of his way to acknowledge the tremendous successes of modern medicine in certain areas (trauma medicine, many areas of surgery). He believes in "the right tool for the right job," and the advances on these fronts are real and valuable and must not be dismissed.

However, when these specific successes are conflated with everything else under the umbrella of allopathic medicine – as if it's all one monolithic enterprise – Dr. Garwood is quick to point out the underlying sleight of hand behind this bait-and-switch. He insists that each discipline in medicine stand on its own two feet, exposed at all times to fair criticism *and competition* – and you should do the same. Uncritical acceptance is the way of the drone or serf, not the self-governed Christian. Letting all of allopathic medicine ride the coattails of legitimate successes in emergency medicine and surgical innovation has led many to discount wholistic medicine.

If defenders of wholistic medicine pointed to one area of success in the field and claimed that the one area of success proves that all of wholistic practice is therefore validated, would you agree? I wouldn't, and you shouldn't either, but how many doctors could object without becoming hypocrites? We need to follow Paul's command, "in understanding, be men" (1 Cor. 14:20) and not be manipulated by faulty logic by anyone on *either* side of the dispute.

The Problem with Monopolistic Power

When the medical enterprise attempts to operate more and more like a monopoly (having a corner on the truth and therefore the only legitimate game in town), it is advancing a doctrine of infallibility in its favor. The claim of infallibility is always exclusive: if I'm right, you must be wrong. The system doesn't even have to use the term "infallible," it need only speak and act as if infallible. The infallible members of your society become the de facto gods of your society. Every competitor is defined to be fallible – and, in fact, dangerously fallible.

The irony, of course, is that modern medicine has been back-pedaling continually for centuries: it is notoriously fallible. There's even a special word to describe illnesses and injuries sustained under treatment by a doctor or a hospital: iatrogenic. But I'm speaking not of individual practitioners but of the system as a whole: today's orthodoxy becomes tomorrow's old wives' tale – except the old wife is actually the mass of doctors of the previous decades. Conventional wisdom is continually overturned.

How can this situation prevail and doctors still retain their air of infallibility? It's not as if being infallible is a plus, because doctors have been subjected to the false idea of infinite liability: gods must be perfect, and any error is savagely penalized. Infinite liability drives up the cost of insurance premiums doctors must pay, making it increasingly difficult to enter certain risky specialties in an era as litigious as our own.

The answer is that Western medicine is quick to loudly put its errors behind it and create the impression that *all its errors lie in the past*. Its defenders will bemoan that Ignaz Semmelweis (1818-1865) was vilified by the medical profession for calling upon surgeons to wash their hands and tools before surgery. Doctors at the time refused to believe that *they* were the source of infection, morbidity, and death. Modern medicine would have you believe these lessons were learned, but new parallels seem to crop up over time.

Let's consider one area where health professionals appeared to be penetrating the area of wholistic medicine: the food pyramid. Each subsequent era saw the previous food pyramid being scorned as erroneous, yet each was put forward as the model for a healthy diet. But medical critics of earlier pyramids asserted that following the earlier guideline would be harmful to one's health. Were the earlier pyramids designed to promote certain products and not others? Have we arrived at the final "healthy" pyramid? How would you know, given that science is always provisional and never final in its claims? Dr. Garwood's wholistic alternative to these fluctuating standards at least has its feet planted firmly in reality.

The monopolistic bent of Western medicine (which comes into focus when Dr. Garwood discusses the Flexner Report herein) is reflected in its antagonism toward competitive systems of healing. The AMA's infamous war against chiropractic ended badly for modern medicine, while the mechanistic models that dominate the horizon made it hard for doctors to understand how acupuncture (based on meridians absent from Western medical charts) could possibly work – yet it can and does. Such concessions don't come easy to the monopolists.

The overturning of conventional wisdom doesn't look good in a monopolistic, infallible system, which is why such systems routinely co-opt each course correction as a positive achievement rather than as proof of earlier institutional blindness. Some course corrections take centuries, and the fact that the error was ancient doesn't fully explain it, it merely tells us how long the researchers were blind to the truth. Let's consider two examples that illuminate this problem.

The physician who exerted the most influence on medicine was Galen (129-217 A.D.), whose impact stretched forward fifteen centuries. His anatomy and physiology weren't challenged until the

17th century. He wrote over 600 treatises, two-thirds of which have been lost, and the index of words used in his works spans 1,300 pages in its own right.[4] What he got right had a huge impact over time, but his errors also radiated down through the centuries too, shaping the future of medicine as well. One blindness of his: he could see blood in arteries and in veins, but had no conception of blood circulation (which waited until 1628 for William Harvey to describe).

If Galen could miss circulation, as massive as his achievements were (and they tower over the medical profession), and surgeons could miss the importance of sterile conditions, how is it that medicine is so certain it hasn't missed anything? The next example puts another nail in the coffin of infallibility.

For several centuries, the heart was thought to be a compression pump, squeezing blood straight into the blood vessels for distribution. But modern non-invasive imaging of the flow of blood in the 21st century showed blood in the heart flowing in very complex rotating patterns: vortices where even individual blood cells are spinning. There is a tremendous amount of angular (rotational) momentum inside the human heart, which would have been unthinkable to previous generations who only saw a simple linear pump. Some of the spiraling blood is critical to keeping certain passages in the heart open and functional. The complexity is stunning, the complex rotational system an astonishment to all who see the imaging videos.

When Dr. Ares Pasipoularides (M.D., Ph.D., FACC) published his 960-page masterpiece, *Heart's Vortex*, in 2010, he disclosed in exhaustive detail what was going on inside the heart – none of which was fully understood prior to that time period.[5]

---

4   Cf. Ares Pasipoularides, "Galen, father of systematic Medicine. An essay on the evolution of modern Medicine and Cardiology," *International Journal of Cardiology*, January 2014, 172(1).

5   Ares Pasipoularides, *Heart's Vortex* (Shelton, CT: People's Medical Publishing House-USA, 2010). Dr. Pasipoularides is Consulting Professor of Surgery, School of Medicine, Duke University, Durham, NC. Formerly, Director of Cardiac Function, Duke/NSF Center for Emerging Cardiovascular

But this scientific discovery isn't the big surprise regarding how the heart actually works (despite contradicting centuries of erroneous concepts dominating the medical field).

The big surprise is that an earlier researcher had *already discovered* the vorticity of blood inside the mammalian heart, but nobody took his findings seriously. Leonardo da Vinci had painstakingly analyzed the flow of blood inside the heart of an ox and sketched out the vortices and their paths in his notebooks. He described phenomena that didn't come to light again until the late 20th century.[6] The dense tech-talk in the previous footnote shows that it took eight doctors to arrive at a scientific conclusion already reached five centuries earlier by da Vinci, who had written that "blood flows out of the ventricle into the sinuses of Valsalva where a portion of the forward flow is diverted to form a vortical flow that assists in the closure of the leaflets of the aortic valve."[7] This idea appears as a "new" discovery in the last footnote.

In short: modern medicine was five centuries behind da Vinci's discovery. Science actually lost ground and went backwards,

---

Technologies, Duke University, Durham, NC. Formerly, Director of Cardiovascular Research at Brooke Army Medical Center, Fort Sam Houston, San Antonio, TX.

6 Ralph Marinelli, et al., "The Heart is Not a Pump: A Refutation of the Pressure Propulsion Premise of Heart Function" in "Frontier Perspectives," *The Journal of the Center for Frontier Sciences at Temple University*, Fall–Winter 1995 (Vol. 5, No. 1). The authors point out that "normal blood flow involved a transfer of momenta via vortical and helical motions, including even the spinning of individual blood cells on their axes in curvilinear streams, the shape of red cells being a testament to the concept." Farhad Bakhtiary, MD, Mirko Schiemann, MD, Omer Dzemali, MD, Selami Dogan, MD, Volker Schachinger, MD, PhD, Hans Ackermann, MD, PhD, Anton Moritz, MD,PhD, Peter Kleine, MD, PhD, "Impact of Patient-Prosthesis Mismatch and Aortic Valve Design on Coronary Flow Reserve after Aortic Valve Replacement," *Journal of the American College of Cardiology*, Vol. 49, No. 7, 2007, inform us that "Normal coronary flow reserve is dependent upon whether or not stable spiral flow, which contains stored momentum, is able to pass through the valve and into the sinuses of Valsalva without disruption."

7 This English paraphrase of da Vinci's original appears in Jack C. Bokros, *Heart of Carbon* (forthcoming in 2021).

failing to observe (with all its instruments) what da Vinci could see without any instruments. As recently as December 2019, Dr. Pasipoularides himself drew attention to this stunning situation.[8] We've ended up back where we were five hundred years ago. Who should get the credit?

These discoveries also illustrate how reductionist thinking (e.g., the heart is merely a simple pump) stymies scientific progress and often makes the truth inaccessible. The profession assumed the matter was inconsequential and unimportant. The experts were wrong on both counts.

We've not even touched on the question of suppression of data by scientific and medical researchers. One of the more notorious cases involved Sigmund Freud, who discounted a massive amount of evidence for incest in the culture he lived in due to confirmation bias against the results of his own research.[9] This issue became heated enough to end up in court when defenders and critics of Freud clashed (the critic won the case).[10]

Small wonder then that Dr. Garwood thinks we should be more discriminating regarding whom – or Whom – we place our faith in when it comes to our spiritual and physical health. Credit where credit is due, yes, but exercise a healthy skepticism when professionals resort to pulling rank and attempt to canonize the status quo.

---

8   Ares Pasipoularides, "Emulating Leonardo da Vinci (1452-1519): the convergence of science and art in biomedical research and practice," *Cardiovascular Research,* December 2019, 115(14):e181-e183.

9   Judith Herman, M.D., *Trauma and Recovery* (New York, NY: Basic Books, 1992, 1997, 2015), 9-20.

10 Jeffrey Masson wrote *The Assault on Truth: Freud's Suppression of the Seduction Theory* in 1984 and was targeted by Allen Esterson, who wrote *The Myth of Freud's Ostracism by the Medical Community 1895-1905.* Masson won a libel suit against *The New Yorker* magazine.

Man is a Unity

One key point that Dr. Garwood makes through this volume is that man was created as a unity. Death is the extraordinary disruption of this unity, the tearing apart of soul and body, which are otherwise fully united. Reductionist-minded theologians and scientists have tried to argue otherwise. The humanistic world-view has tried to exorcise "the ghost in the machine," the soul in the body, so to speak, to prove we're molecules in motion and that everything reduces to matter.

It is noteworthy that some key humanist scholars have debunked their colleagues' position on this point. Dr. Noam Chomsky discredits any claimed success for this strategy:

> [Cartesian dogma] is commonly derided today as the belief that there is "a ghost in the machine." But that conclusion mistakes what happened. It was the Cartesian theory of body that collapsed; the theory of mind, such as it was, remained unaffected. Newton ... had nothing to say about the ghost in the machine; he exorcised the machine, not the ghost.[11]

Yet humanists continue to operate in terms of a discredited premise anyway.

Studies of the effects of emotional trauma on the human body have illustrated that the two domains (the mental and physical) are not distinct and separated, walled off from one another. Rather, they affect each other in powerful ways. For example, under threat, a normal person's adrenal glands will finally release cortisol. The adrenal glands of a person who has suffered from emotional trauma will not release cortisol in that situation. This release of cortisol is an important part of a key chemical cascade[12] and its absence illus-

---

11   Noam Chomsky, *Language and Thought* (Wakefield, RI: Moyer Bell, 1993), 81.

12   Babette Rothschild, *The Body Remembers: The Psychophysiology of Trauma and*

trates how the body and the mind are tightly united in ways that continue to surprise modern researchers. It is significant that this effect involves a body subsystem that Dr. Garwood addresses often in this book: the autonomic nervous system (ANS). Fortunately for the reader, Dr. Garwood keeps things simple and easy to understand – unlike some technical points being made in this foreword.

One important consequence of holding to the unity of man's nature is that all aspects of man's being can be dealt with in terms of health. This is important in that health denotes wholeness, and it is the whole man that needs to be made whole, to be treated as a whole and not as isolated parts.

Healing: External or Internal?

One of the most valuable lessons Dr. Garwood imparts to the reader is that in most cases the body has the tools to heal itself, so the proper approach is to facilitate, enable, and expedite[13] these

---

Trauma Treatment, (New York, NY: W. W. Norton & Co., 2000), 8-12. The cascade occurs on the HPA (Hypothalamic-Pituitary-Adrenal) axis. Cortisol is required to "fix" the event in memory as being in the past – without the cortisol release, the event floats in time and persists into the present. The mind has an effect on the body, and the body has an effect upon the mind. More recent research on these phenomena can be found in Bessel A. van der Kolk, *The Body Keeps the Score* (New York, NY: Penguin Books, 2014), pp. 208ff where brain scans illustrate structural changes in the brain as a result of emotional trauma. Such conceptions would have been laughed at as unscientific gibberish not too many decades ago, and yet the brain scans do not lie.

13 For example, basal cell carcinomas – a form of skin cancer – used to always entail either surgical removal or liquid nitrogen freezing, which are allopathic steps taken against the cancer. A more recent innovation is Imiquimod cream, which is applied to the cancer and the region around it. The cream signals the body that an invader is present, acting as a whistle blower, sounding the trumpet in a biological call-to-arms. In turn, the body's defenses concentrate around the cancer and destroy it completely. Here is a case where modern medicine has taken a step away from allopathy, harnessing the body's own defenses and assisting them by putting them on the scent of the cancer. While not suitable for every location in the body, such innovations make

internal processes, not introduce foreign agents into the mix to elbow the body's mechanisms out of the way to do indiscriminate battle against whatever problem has arisen.

At one level, we all accept this idea. A suture is a way to help the body heal itself after a laceration: it holds the severed tissues together long enough for the wound to be repaired by the body's own resources. When a bone is broken, medical doctors don't create a brand new bone: they set the bone to align the ends so the body itself can do the repair by reuniting the ends. (When a structure is lost and replaced with a prosthetic or artificial unit, the performance is almost always inferior to the original. Yes, a titanium joint may be stronger, but it has no marrow to create new blood cells for the recipient.)

As for the power of nutrition (the first of three key elements in Dr. Garwood's assessment, which includes Nutrify, Detox, and Energize), this power has been recognized for several centuries in cases we instantly recognize. Scurvy is what happens when you suffer from a vitamin C deficiency, rickets and beriberi occur when vitamins D or B1, respectively, are in short supply. However, we've compartmentalized this knowledge rather than expanded its significance. Are these the only deficiencies we need to concern ourselves with? What other deficiencies are working under the surface due to factors we've not considered? It is in this area that this volume is particularly useful, as it delineates the full range of items the body needs (the author's exhaustive *mighty ninety* list of nutrients). Nothing slips through the cracks here.

Some Christians might question the importance of such physical care of God's temple, and oftentimes a misunderstanding of 1 Timothy 4:8 is the culprit. While true that eternal things are weightier than temporal things, that doesn't mean temporal things have no weight whatsoever. By the same token, when Paul says that "bodily exercise profiteth little," it is only in comparison to spiritual

---

surgeries (and subsequent loss of healthy tissue to gain adequate margins around the cancer) a thing of the past in many cases. Of course, when the body goes to war against a cancer, the skin *looks* like a war zone for a while – which is why prevention is always better than treatment after the fact.

things that the word "little" is used. Even so, the translation might read more accurately as "bodily exercise benefits in a few things, but devoutness is beneficial in all things."[14] As Patrick Fairbairn said of Paul's point, action taken to sustain physical health "was profitable within a certain limited sphere, since it contributed to the healthfulness and agility of the physical frame."[15]

Controversies – or are they?

It is important to always read with discernment, to "eat the meat but spit out the bones." This volume is a pioneering effort, and it is self-understood that "the pioneer is the guy with an arrow in his back."

But one thing we have already seen is that medical science has spit out meat it thought was bones, and has swallowed its fair share of bones (not all of which it has detected). We should exercise the same care in considering Dr. Garwood's more controversial claims, especially if we have a background in Western medicine and would find it challenging to abstain from scoffing or dismissing some of his discussions. Not every subject is settled, and we shouldn't lead with our ignorance (which always comes back to bite us).

Let us conclude with a consideration of two of the more controversial aspects covered in this volume: detoxing and electricity, the first from a scriptural perspective, the second from a scientific point of view.

Controversy 1: Detoxing

A shallow reading of Dr. Garwood's discussion on detoxing and his comparison of detoxing to the mortification of sin may strike the theologically astute reader as a bit of a stretch. It appears

---

14 The term "bodily exercise" appears in the Greek as *somatic gymnasia* and likely includes all exertions taken for the sake of one's health, not merely physical activity (although that would be included under that heading).

15 Patrick Fairbairn, *The Pastoral Epistles* (Edinburgh: T & T Clark, 1874), 181-182.

that he's drawing a very tenuous analogy, and some may consider it a forced fit, as if he were equating things gratuitously and without adequate foundation.

The skeptic might demand, "Can you show me detoxing in scripture?" with the assumption that no scripture could be put forward to satisfy this challenge.

But this challenge suffers from the same problem as the challenge that the Pharisees issued to Nicodemus in John 7:52. They told him, "Search, and look: for out of Galilee ariseth no prophet." Their starting assumption was that the Scriptures nowhere spoke of a prophet coming from Galilee. Stunningly, they missed Isaiah 9:1-7, which specifically mentions Galilee in connection with the Messiah.

What does the detox process entail? The removal of one thing from the body, so that the body in turn would be in a cleansed state. And it turns out that this concept can be found in the text of Mark 7:19, where the term for the discharging of the impure matter from the body (*ekporeuetai*) is directly adjacent to the verb for the resulting cleansing process (*katharizoon*). As J. A. Alexander puts it:

> … that part of the process of digestion which is most offensive is in fact a purifying one, because it carries off the impure portion of the food, leaving only what is nutritive and healthful.[16]

Herman Ridderbos confirms this as the correct analysis of Christ's comment:

> *katharizoon* must be taken as the continuation of *ekporeuetai*. The process of digestion is at the same time the purification of the food![17]

---

16 Joseph Addison Alexander, *The Gospel According to Mark* (Grand Rapids, MI: Baker Book House, 1858 [1980]), 193-194.

17 Herman Ridderbos, *The Coming of the Kingdom* (Nutley, NJ: Presbyterian & Reformed, 1962), 332.

And H. A. W. Meyer affirms the same meaning:

[This process] … makes pure the whole of the food (that is eaten), inasmuch, namely, as thereby every impurity passes away from it (by mean of the excrements).[18]

Removal of impurities, of offensive things, so that pure things remain is, by definition, detoxing. This technical discussion by our Lord is considered by some scholars[19] to be a "coarse" explanation (as to subject matter) but it is nonetheless carefully worded by Him.

Consequently, when Dr. Garwood discusses the process of removing impure things from the body, of detoxification, he cannot be accused of asserting things not found, in conceptual form, in the Word of God itself. The Scriptures are no stranger to this concept – the removal of dross from silver, etc., is even a Messianic theme – but in Mark 7:19 the concept is clearly associated with a major bodily function.

We would conclude, then, that the detox process is discussed in Scripture in all but name, that its purification by removal of impurities can be no less corporeal as it is spiritual, and that these two aspects of the idea are both important to retain in our understanding.

Controversy 2: Electricity

Individuals with a background in electromagnetic theory may find some of Dr. Garwood's concepts (which he credits and attributes to his source materials) difficult to accept. This circumstance arises because we're not normally confronted with overt electrical phenomena in the biological sciences (with the exception of the electric eel, etc.).

While we will readily grant that EKGs read electrical signals in the heart, and EEGs read electrical signals in the brain, we tend to

---

18 Heinrich Augustus Wilhelm Meyer, *Critical and Exegetical Hand-Book to the Gospels of Mark and Luke* (Winona Lake, IN: Alpha Publications, 1980, first published by T & T Clark in 1883), 90.
19 E.g., Lutheran scholar R. C. H. Lenski.

leave it there. At the much smaller scale of the individual cell, we're willing to accept chemical activity at that level, but not electrical activity. The skeptic sees this as a force-fit and thus pseudo-scientific, as Dr. Garwood isn't using technical terms to describe voltage potentials within the cell or explaining their precise significance. The book, after all, is an *introduction* to a wide-ranging sweep of topics and not the last word.

But the importance of electric and magnetic fields in the biological sciences is itself a growing area of research. The continent-long migrations of birds and insects is evidently made possible because these creatures can detect the Earth's magnetic field and navigate with reference to it (the sensors in the higher animals is often in their nose – as if they're "following their nose"). Further, whenever massive electromagnets are built (such as in particle accelerators or plasma containment systems), people are wise to stay far away from them. The deleterious effects can be quite dangerous.

Electrical research by earlier scientists has yielded plenty of surprises that sometimes defy easy explanation. For example, the Earth has an electric field, and one of the first experiments carried aloft on a hot-air balloon was a gold-foil electrometer to confirm that the voltage would decrease as the balloon got higher. In actual fact, *the voltage increased* the higher up the balloon soared, which came as a totally unexpected shock to the researchers.

Legendary researcher Nicola Tesla set up an experiment to see if he could pump enough electrical energy into the Earth to make it vibrate electrically. To his surprise, he discovered that the required energy was already present.

In times past, astrophysicists noted that the spiral arms of galaxies were not winding up as expected, and it wasn't long before electric fields were being postulated to account for the observed behaviors in our night sky.

None of these facts, per se, prove that the electrical ideas Dr. Garwood puts on the table for the reader's consideration are correct. But these facts illustrate that when it comes to electricity, the final chapter in that story has yet to be written. And when that is the case (barring irrefutable measurements to the contrary), we'd be wise not to dismiss new ideas too hastily – especially in light of the various scientific missteps described above.

Throughout the history of science, inconvenient facts get pushed off to the side so as not to pose too great a challenge to the status quo theories.[20] Confirmation bias blinds in both directions: you only see what you want, and you blind yourself to opposing data or (at the very least) its significance.

What, therefore, is the issue with voltages within the cells of the human body?

Scientists will freely admit that there is electrical activity in structures larger than the cell, and even between cells (the nervous system sends signals using electrical depolarization waves) but not inside the cell. On what basis is *that* boundary imposed? It appears to be imposed due to confirmation bias and paradigm reinforcement. Only experiment and measurement should be allowed the prerogative to set aside these ideas in favor of a better one. Our science, like our faith, should be ever-reforming to be closer to the truth.

In his book, *Exegetical Fallacies*, D. A. Carson speaks of the logical fallacy of *cavalier dismissal*, when a position isn't refuted but merely written off. When it comes to the health of our families and ourselves, we should avoid building our lives on such a fallacy. There is a crucible of innovation in the world of Wholistic medicine, a world where spiritual discernment and avoiding the errors of past centuries can be freely exercised.

---

20 It has become popular among defenders of scientism to launch scathing attacks against Karl Popper and Thomas Kuhn, who had identified problems in how scientists conduct their work and build and market their theories, but this is largely the result of the increasingly politicized nature of science. Such politicization works in favor of monopolization and tyranny in the health sector. That science would bend the knee to political correctness is a disturbing trend of our times, undermining any remaining trust we may have for the priests in white lab coats.

Conclusion

Quackery is a strong word. In the medical field, there is no more pejorative descriptor than "quack." Because it's a strong word, it's important that we understand what true quackery is. R. J. Rushdoony provides sound guidance here:

> The difference between a quack doctor and a good one begins with a sense of limitation. A quack medicine and a quack doctor both promise too much. A sound medicine offers limited help for a limited and specific problem. It offers no miracles and works none. It cannot replace good hygiene, sound nutrition, and healthy habits. The wise doctor makes no large promises; he knows how limited his role is, and yet, *within those limits, very important.* The more we demand of a doctor or of medicine, the more likely we are to fall prey to quackery.
>
> We have quackery all around us, in the church, the school, and in politics. … It is present wherever men offer something short of God's Word as the bread of life.[21]

Western medicine has lost its *sense of limitation*, and one way it *promises too much* is by denying any benefit to competing healing systems.[22] Whereas Dr. Garwood puts *good hygiene, sound nutrition, and healthy habits* front and center, much of allopathic medicine seeks ways to ease the consequences of neglecting them. And when Western medicine sees man mechanistically, as molecules in motion, it will necessarily *offer something short of God's Word as the bread of life.*

In contrast, the author of this book has focused on the primacy of God's Word as controlling every aspect of life. He holds, teaches, and lives out a faith for all of life, and has written a wonder-

---

21 https://chalcedon.edu/magazine/the-principles-and-practice-of-quackery
22 This is achieved directly but also indirectly, using bureaucratic barriers. See Dr. Garwood's discussion of the Flexner Report in the body of this volume for further insights.

ful survey describing a vision for health for all of life. He focuses on *establishing* health first, and *recovering* health only as needed.

In the great dispute between the two main theories governing the medical enterprise (Pasteur's *germ theory* versus Beauchamp's *terrain theory*), Dr. Garwood articulates a compelling defense of the latter, the importance of which can be grasped once it is understood that only one of these lends itself to Christian self-government. You can govern your own internal terrain by your own hand, but the germ model requires delegation to others (which is being increasingly mandated by coercive state action).

Christian self-government is the antidote to coercive statism in every dimension, including health and healing. We have here, finally, a book that provides a good set of starting blueprints to implement such a wide-ranging self-government, one which embraces responsibility rather than delegating it. It leads by example. It surveys multiple sources and is necessarily derivative, serving as a gateway for deeper research by the reader, but those are strengths and not weaknesses of Dr. Garwood's approach.

May the reader of this book grasp the value of the counsel offered by the author, and labor for the future described in Ezekiel 47:1-12, where the spread of His Kingdom's living waters shall bring healing to the entire world.

Martin G. Selbrede

Vice President and Resident Scholar at the Chalcedon Foundation
Editor, *Faith for All of Life*, *Arise & Build*, and *The Chalcedon Report*
Supervising Editor, *Journal of Christian Liberty*
www.chalcedon.edu

PREFACE

The phrase 'health for all of life' didn't originate with me, but once I was introduced to it, I found myself enamored by the concept. Due to my theological presuppositions and my exasperating insistence on developing and applying a 'faith for all of life,' the phrase fit hand-in-glove with where my passions already lie. In my view, the kingdom of God ought to encompass and envelope every aspect of life—all of Christ, for all of life—and since that's where I'm at *anyway*, I might as well, I thought, deal with the issue of health. Abraham Kuyper famously told us that there's not one square inch that exists on this earth where Christ doesn't cry, "Mine!" To which I say, *amen*.

I owe a great deal to Rev. John T. (Jack) Campbell Jr. of *Reformed Ministries International* who developed much of the latter half of this book, integrating it into his CASTLE discipleship program. It was Bill Evans who introduced me to Jack and the website HealthForAllOfLife.com. The funny thing is, much of everything on the site I was already doing thanks to my wife, Mary. We had already included much of the content in our home seeking natural ways to heal rather than rely on the allopathic industry which we knew from experience was a train wreck.

In September of 2019 I preached a sermon called "Vaccines: The Gospel Imperative to End the Silence." Those who know me know that I take very seriously the gospel of the Kingdom and thus I believe pulpits should be applying the Bible in ways that seem rather unconventional. (If Christ is Lord of all, and he most certainly is, then why in the world are we so silent on so many issues?) So, I researched and read, wrote a sermon, and even had Dr. Suzanne Humphries review the manuscript. She offered up a few clarifying corrections and thanked me for preaching the message. Preparing a sermon like this took a lot of time and effort, and I am thankful for everything I have learned and continue to learn. However, it wasn't enough. More research needed to happen. I wasn't finished learning.

A month or so later my friend Chris and I attended a large anti-vaccine/pro-medical freedom rally in Washington D.C. which featured people like Del Bigtree from *The Highwire*, Robert F. Kennedy Jr., Mary Holland, and Dr. Sherri Tenpenny. On our way home that evening, I told Chris that I wanted to expand my vaccine sermon into a book of its own, if only I could get the financial help necessary to do the project. Little did I know that the Holy Spirit was already at work.

The next day my friend Bill called and told me that he wanted me to write a book expanding what I had said in the vaccine sermon to include the content on the HealthForAllOfLife.com website. He envisaged me taking my theological convictions and marrying them to the seven cell-building essentials. He told me that I was the only one who could write the book, which made me both nervous and excited. To recap: less than 24 hours after I voiced my desire to have this book project underwritten, Bill calls to tell me that he is going to help make sure it happens. Talk about the Providence of God!

So, naturally, I went down the rabbit hole and began reading more and more, watching just about every single video listed on the website. I spent hours upon hours reading thousands and thousands of pages from various natural doctors and health professionals (listed in Appendix 1 & 3). Because this was a clear direction from God the Holy Spirit, I had the motivation and energy to see it through. The book you are holding is a manifesto, a declaration outlining how the nations can be healed, and I'm thankful you have chosen to join me for the ride. May the Lord receive the glory, and may the promise of Matthew 28:18-20 be fulfilled:

Then Jesus came and spoke to them, saying, "All authority has been given to Me in heaven and on earth. Go therefore and make disciples of all nations, baptizing them in the name of the Father and of the Son and of the Holy Spirit, teaching them to observe all things I have commanded you. And remember, I am with you always, even to the end of the age." Amen.

Rev. Dr. Jason M. Garwood
Warrenton, VA
September 10, 2020

INTRODUCTION

"The effective, fervent prayer of a righteous
man accomplishes much."
James 5:16b

I should probably warn you up front: this manifesto is deeply personal for me. My wife Mary has fought for nearly a decade to rid herself of Lyme Disease and a laundry list of other coinfections. She has, out of necessity, become her own doctor. I have followed her example in taking ownership over *my* health, too, and by God's grace, we are teaching our three children to do the same. The book is personal because, as you would suspect, we have been on quite a journey. Between detoxing the metals left in our bodies from vaccines and trying to eat properly for nutrition's sake, our journey has been more akin to a fight. The fight is ongoing and like any battle, you need proper weapons of war. The concepts and practical suggestions offered in the following pages are weapons we have found to be safe, effective, and cost efficient. The safety, effectiveness, and cost of modern medicine is a gamble *at best*. Not here. The protocols are safe, the procedures are most definitely effective, and—believe you me—they are much, much cheaper than anything Big Pharma has to offer. I hope and pray you will join me in laying out a vision for hope and healing for the nations.

Have you ever taken the time to notice that the overwhelming majority of prayer requests in our churches have something to do with health and healing? Pray for Aunt Betty who has been dealing with a six-week cold. Pray for Jim who fell at work and still can't get his back pain to go away despite several surgeries and pain kill-ers. Pray for Sue's cousin's niece who, at the age of seven, has lym-phoma. Pray for Frank's boss who just learned that he has diabetes. And on and on we go. If I were a betting man, I'd say that upwards of 95% of all prayer requests in our local churches are about sickness and disease—the very thing most pastors and elders are unequipped to deal with. What are we to do? Should we uncritically raise the white flag and accept defeat? Do we pray with vigor and faith and leave the results solely to God? Or might we consider doing some-thing before those requests hit the prayer chain? This book seeks to answer those questions.

TIME TO WAKE UP

It is high time we acknowledge the truth of our current pre-dicament. We live in the twenty-first century and boast in our seem-ingly inexhaustible knowledge: we have gigabyte internet down-load/upload capabilities which helps us transfer massive amounts of information in seconds; we can split atoms and make tremendous amounts of energy; and we have—thanks to the free market (which isn't so free anymore!)—incredible access to medicine, doctors, and technology (MRI machines, bio-scanning technologies, etc.). Our information-age tower-of-Babel boasts of so many things, yet we have a major problem on our hands: everyone is sick, over-drugged with chemical synthetics, woefully malnourished, and no one in the contemporary field of medicine has a 'cure' for cancer and chronic illness—despite the billions of dollars 'invested' for research. As I write this, Merck has approval from the FDA to develop a live-vi-rus Ebola vaccine,[23] and as of 2018, the Center for Disease Control (CDC) reports that 1 in 59 children has autism. Right now, the world is talking about the so-called coronavirus which has a differ-ent origin story from week to week. We think we've made tremen-

---

23 https://www.greenmedinfo.health/blog/fda-approves-mercks-new-live-ebola-vaccine-which-it-says-can-shed-and-cause-immun (accessed January 2, 2020).

dous progress in the field of bio-engineering, medicine, and health-care, however, we're dying of Alzheimer's disease, heart disease is still the number one killer[24], and for some reason we still want to purchase the medicine we see on television commercials that may help with one particular condition, but are guaranteed to give you a laundry list of other issues. *It's time to wake up.*

We have a responsibility problem, or, I should say, a self-government problem. We don't take responsibility for our spiritual health and well-being -- after all, we have religious specialists for that. We don't take responsibility for our intellectual health and well-being -- after all, we have educational and media specialists to think for us. For the most part, we don't take responsibility for our physical health -- after all, we have medical specialists to make our decisions for us. We have, in each of these areas, placed ourselves in neutral, allowing ourselves to float as if in an inner tube out in the middle of the Atlantic.

To make matters worse, we have civil rulers, what we might call 'specialists in power', seeking to control and regulate all of the previously mentioned specialists. Specialists in charge of other specialists who are in charge of *you*. Today we have government bureaucrats controlling air quality, food quality, education quality, and medical quality. As if it could get any worse, we have government 'public health officials' and 'regulators' who pass through the revolving door of the highly profitable pharmaceutical-medical mafia, too. Their goal is to control and virtually mandate medical treatment for everyone. In short: we haven't just let the medical boards and bureaucrats take the wheel; we have jumped out of the car while they drive off into the billion-dollar sunset.

---

24 There is debate on these numbers. When we consider the destruction of children in the womb (both abortion and IVF procedures), the numbers are staggering. The number one 'killer' of image bearers is actually medical doctors, through medical mistakes, misdiagnoses, and actual abortion procedures. Included in these 'medical mistakes' are the prescriptions for things like statin drugs, chemotherapy, and other synthetic drugs which wreak havoc on unsuspecting recipients.

Since we exist on this earth to glorify God, and because we carry out this worship in our physical bodies, nothing is more fundamental to that purpose than our physical health. Since we are spiritual creatures equipped with material bodies (that is partly what it means to be human and made in the image of God), we can conclude that one cannot do much without a healthy, fully functioning body. We only receive one of these bodies, issued from heaven at the moment of conception. Yet, surprisingly, most of us simply do not have even the most basic understanding of how our bodies work, or how God has designed our bodies to *keep working*—even though we readily admit that we are 'fearfully and wonderfully made' (Ps. 139:14).

Likewise, we have little knowledge about or experience in using the amazing assortment of minerals, nutrients, plants, healing agents, etc., that God has placed here in his creation in order to support and supplement our strength, health, vitality, healing, and general well-being. Because we don't know what we don't know, and because we cannot share with others something we do not possess, we are, sadly, surrounded by friends, family, loved ones, and image-bearing strangers who suffer from a myriad of chronic illness and health problems—and we feel *powerless* to help them. They perish for a lack of knowledge (Hosea 4:6), and it is our fault, too.

HealthForAllOfLife.com, a website which sifts through the natural health world, giving you easy access to Wholistic doctors and the material in this book, was created to correct the problem of ignorance by offering a massive injection of Vitamin-I (information!). It will teach you simple, safe, effective, preventative, and affordable ways to not only stay healthy, but to minister good news to the sick and suffering, and treat conditions and cure diseases that the billion-dollar-a-year medical industrial complex simply cannot cure, nor *desires* to cure. Who in their right mind solves a problem in the market which will lead to your company's collapse? That's not a great business plan, now is it? In fact, these interests only make things worse! And why do they make things worse? Because they don't know the Creator, *the* Great Physician, and they don't know His amazing provisions for your physical health and well-being.

That, and they only treat symptoms, but we're getting ahead of ourselves. The truth is, *it's time to get our car back.* Your health belongs to *you.* It is *your* responsibility.

Speaking of cars, stay with me for a quick thought experiment and illustration. Imagine trying to keep your car's engine in fully operational shape by going to a tarot card reader for help. The engine, we know, had a designer, and we would do well to not only acknowledge the designer, but to consult him and follow his protocols, too. Your car's engine doesn't work on voodoo and an astrology of luck and chance. It runs *by design.* It needs gasoline, oil, and regular preventative maintenance.

The difference between the car engine and your body is rather self-explanatory. The engineer who designed the engine wasn't capable of building into the structure of the engine a metaphysical, life-giving and sustaining soul, or a microbiological, electrical/ neurological, respiratory, muscular, circulatory, lymphatic, chemical information storage and retrieval system (DNA), and immune system to monitor and repair itself, which is what God has given our bodies. If we want the engine that is our body to work, we need to check the blueprints and plans the designer has given us. *Health for All of Life* is my effort at pointing us back to the blueprints.

HOW TO READ THIS BOOK

The purpose of this book is threefold:

1) **When you're sick, you're out of the fight, and thus you're not fulfilling your God-given calling**. The sad truth is that we here in America are the sickest we've ever been, and that's in spite of the vaccine industry's declaration that they are the ones who have single-handedly defeated polio, measles, etc. In a nation plagued with chronic conditions, cancers, and out of control childhood illness, can we really call this a success? The fact is, when you're sick, you're out of the fight. What is the fight? *The*

great calling and vocation to expand the kingdom of God into every area of life by making all nations disciples who are baptized into the covenant and taught to obey everything Christ has commanded (Matt. 28:18-20). When we are sick, we are prohibited from fulfilling our individual purpose for the kingdom of God, which means we need to remove this impediment by taking our health seriously and restoring the fundamental calling of self-government in the arena of health and vivacity.

2) **The resurrection of Jesus in the middle of history has outdone and surpassed the damage incurred by Adam's sin.** The Second Person of the Trinity took on human flesh and dwelt among us, planting God's flag in space and time, declaring that earth is now going to gradually become God's dwelling place. Jesus Christ came on a mission—a search and rescue mission no less—and in doing so reclaimed the world from the forces of Satan, sin, and death in order to establish an immovable kingdom of righteousness and peace, justice and *longevity*. In light of the fact that sin has been comprehensively distributed to the world, we need to know that the gospel goes much, much further. Comprehensive problems require a comprehensive gospel and world and life view. As the wonderful Christmas song goes, "he comes to make his blessings flow, *far as the curse is found.*" What I need you to know, dear reader, is that the resurrection of Christ is why we can speak of health and wellness, and it is the working paradigm for the entire book. Christ the King intends to rid the world of sin, sickness, and death. *His* resurrection is *our* down payment. Jesus was in the business of healing people because healing is central to the kingdom of God. And healing is central to the kingdom of God because the world is in need of *restoration*.

3) **It is your job to exercise Godly dominion in the world and the foremost way to do so is by taking control of your own health rather than leaving it to MDs.** The gospel gives a man responsibility for his actions. If you lack the self-control to refrain from consuming a gross amount of sugar, then we have a gospel issue. Your body is a temple, and this means it is your job to take care of it (1 Corinthians 6:19-20). *Aspartame included.* What we want to see are individuals exercising self-control and self-discipline in the arena of health and wellness, and this is because you have a remarkable task before you: discipling the nations. If you're lethargic and gluttonous, you're not going to be equipped for battle. We need to be able to exercise dominion and if you don't have dominion over your *own* body, you're not going to have stewardship-dominion in the other areas God has assigned you to (e.g., education, politics, business, and so on). It starts with *you.* Just like you wouldn't delegate your spiritual health to whatever your pastor says, you shouldn't mindlessly farm out your biological health to the medical doctors. God has created you as a whole person, and he has conscripted *you* into his army. He wants healthy soldiers. He's given us what we need for life and godliness (2 Peter 1:3), so it is time we take this seriously.

I'm writing this book with several different types of readers in mind. There are those who are sick because they *don't* know better (the problem of unconscious ignorance), and those who are sick and *do* know better (the problem of self-government). There are those who don't know what they don't know, and they refuse to be confused by the facts. And then there are those who are desperately searching for answers and the current medical landscape has turned up short. Perhaps you are a God-fearing Christian, or perhaps you are an unconvinced skeptic. Either way, this book is for you. I'm also hoping to reach healthy people, too, as I would be delighted to enlist them in the battle against state-controlled medicine (more on this in Appendix 2).

The book is laid out in a self-consciously ordered fashion. My vision for it is to have both the theology (Part One) and the practical (Part Two), so you're going to see both. I have intentionally written this book so you can have the theological foundation necessary for developing a fully orbed Christian worldview, and so you can have the tools necessary to carry forth this worldview in the day-to-day. Some will be tempted to skip part one and jump right into part two. *Try not to do this.* There is a purposeful flow of thought and after finishing the book, you can certainly skip around to find what you need. Here's what you can expect.

Chapter one is a wholistic treatment of the gospel message and its implications because only a wholistic gospel is going to give us what we need for wholistic healing. This book is like building a house, and I am laying the most important foundation in chapter one. Many well-intentioned people fail to see the connection between the good news of Jesus Christ and how that good news works in the world, especially when it comes to health and the battle against the humanist worldview behind modern medicine. I'm going to help those folks. This is not merely a fight against money-hungry pharmaceutical companies, easily manipulated doctors, and coffer-filling lobbyists in Washington D.C. This is a battle of worldviews and since you can't beat something with nothing, I intend to give you that *something*. Psalm 127:1 is apt for this building project: "Unless the LORD builds the house, they labor in vain who build it."

Chapter two will deal with the theological principles of self-government and God's vision for the healing of the nations. It is important to know that man is *not* an evolved machine, but instead he is a wholly created being made in the image of God whose self-government is foundational to his purpose. This purpose and labor for the kingdom is the bedrock for individual and national healing. If we want to see a revival in the arena of health, we're going to need a whole lot of repentance, as the two things are inextricably tied together, as you'll see.

Chapter three will kick off part two of the book by seeking to answer two questions: What is health? What is sickness? Believe it or not, the allopathic medical establishment does not have the correct definitions for either words. If we are going to deal with sickness, we need to know what it is we are trying to get rid of. If we are going to get healthy, we need to know which goal we are trying to reach. Definitions, then, absolutely matter. Important to our understanding of health and sickness is knowing how we got here, which means we're going to do some history as well. This chapter will introduce you to the science of basic biology and the seven-key cell-building essentials which will set the stage for the rest of the book.

Chapter four is all about nutrition. The 'Mighty 90' is pivotal to cell-building and overall health, which means getting proper nutrition is incredibly important. Much like feeding on Christ (the Bread of Life) in order to be filled spiritually, we need to feed on proper nutrition in order to be filled physically. The MDs today know virtually nothing about nutrition and eating fruits and vegetables doesn't really give the pharmaceutical companies any patentable material. No patent, no money.

Chapter five will deal with detoxification which is largely ignored in our time. Like mortifying sin in order to be spiritually healthy, we need to detox our bodies of neurotoxins, foreign antigens, metals, fungus, synthetic drugs, etc., in order to be physically healthy. Detoxing is largely ignored in the allopathic field and this is because putting chemical toxins in your body is both profitable and central to their world and life view.

Chapter six is about energy and developing different rhythms and practices in order to have a fully functioning nervous system, circulatory system, immune system, etc., so you can feel well and perform well. Like the Holy Spirit who energizes us for love and good deeds, we need proper nutrition, sleep/rest, strong bones, etc., in order to have the necessary energy to expend on the Kingdom.

After the conclusion, where we'll wrap up the housing project, I'm going to give you a few appendices to consider. Appendix 1 is the 'Poor Man's Medicine Cabinet' with some recommendations and 'must haves' for your home. Appendix 2 is the need to address government-controlled medicine with the tips on getting in the fight. This is a 'love God' and 'love your neighbor' fight, as you'll see. Appendix 3 is entitled, 'Meet the Faculty,' and this is simply an introduction to the doctors and professionals whose lectures, books, and websites can be found on the HealthForAllOfLife.com website. The website is a virtual/online medical center. It's a learning experience with the tools you need get your health back in line so that you can fulfill your individual purpose in the kingdom of God. I encourage you to bookmark the site and visit it often.

Appendix 4 is an article I wrote pertaining to humanism, and it is a more in-depth type of read. Some of you may not like that sort of thing, others might want to dive right in. I included it because it helps us understand the worldview which sits behind and controls the menacing problem of statism, which is the fuel for the BigPharma fire.

Before we jump in, I'd like to thank you, my reader, for making the effort to get this book. I encourage you to check out the website *HealthForAllOfLife.com* for more information. In fact, this book is really just a giant sign meant to point you to the website, so be sure to go there and load up on the information! And don't be dead end to the knowledge, either. Help spread the word. Vitamin-I is so crucial to our day. It is absolutely imperative that we think through these issues in order to serve Christ and serve others. This book intends to correct our current condition of wide-spread sickness and illness by offering a better way, a path to wholistic healing and increased productivity, all for the kingdom of God. Buy some copies and give them away. Share a copy with a friend. And lastly, thank you for helping us get the word out. This is a Christian manifesto of hope and healing, so let's get to work on taking dominion over our health!

PART ONE

Orthodoxy
& Understanding

The creation reflects the orderly character of God the Creator. The perceived disorder is in part the product of man's fallen mind and in part the product of God's curse of the world. But Christianity must proclaim the historical reality of Christ's resurrection and ascension. This resurrection leads in history to the progressive transformation and liberation of nature from God's curse, just as surely as the Fall of Adam led in history to a discontinuous transformation and enslavement of nature. To preach the triumph of the curse is to deny the triumph of Christ at Calvary. To construct a methodology of science in terms of the historically irrevocable effects of the second law of thermodynamics is to ignore a fundamental doctrine of the Christian faith.[25]

Gary North

---

25 Gary North, *Is the World Running Down?* (Tyler, Texas: Institute for Christian Economics, 1988), pp. 176-177.

CHAPTER ONE

The King Jesus Gospel

"Now, brothers, I declare to you the gospel which I preached to you, which you have received, and in which you stand. Through it you are saved, if you keep in memory what I preached to you, unless you have believed in vain. For I delivered to you first of all that which I also received: how Christ died for our sins according to the Scriptures, was buried, rose again the third day according to the Scriptures."

-The Apostle Paul: 1 Corinthians 15:1-4

Like it or not, we're in the middle of an ancient war with one basic enemy and only one side that is guaranteed to win. This historical conflict dates back to the early chapters of the book of Genesis when Adam and Eve decided to take matters into their own hands and become a law unto themselves. The enemy? Humanism. The winner? *The risen Christ and His covenant people.*

Keep in mind how God designed the world to function. He created everything 'good' and when he made Adam and Eve, it was 'very good.' The crown of his creation, mankind was to serve God as prophets, priests, and kings under God's sovereignly gentle rule. Man was made in the image of God which means that Adam and Eve and their children's children were to reflect the glory of God by obediently laboring for God's Kingdom franchise. They were God's newly acquired business partners. They were created healthy, happy, and holy—the three important h's. As a set apart people, humankind was to grow in their knowledge of the Lord creating businesses, exploring free market enterprise, manufacturing goods, understanding molecular biology, and distributing their services. This Kingdom enterprise was and is man's *purpose*. Image bearing is a vocational calling to spread the holiness and righteousness of God into every area of life. But something went terribly wrong.

Satan the deceiver introduced to God's image bearers the idea of autonomy, which means 'self-law.' "*Then the serpent said to the woman, 'You surely will not die! For God knows that on the day you eat of it your eyes will be opened and you will be like God, knowing good and evil*" (Gen. 3:4-5). The 'knowing good and evil' part ought to be understood as 'determining' good and evil. Instead of being God's holy subordinates working for God and His Kingdom plan for the world, Adam and Eve swapped their image bearing responsibilities for a life of selfish ambition and self-determination. No longer would they desire to follow God and His law; they wanted to be a law unto themselves. They wanted autonomy; they believed the lie—exchanging the truth about God for the lie of the serpent (Rom. 1:18-35).

The fuel for the engine of humanism is this desire to govern one's own life according to one's own standards and preferences. It is the forsaken aspiration to become not just *as* god, but *a* god. Humanism is the attempt to dethrone God. As a result of their rebellious lust, Adam and Eve plunged the world into sickness, sin, and death. Work became frustrating. Our cells would become deficient of nutrients and thus pathogens and cancers and disease would make their ugly appearance. The world wouldn't function the same anymore because sin—which literally means 'missing the mark'—would become the new working reality and condition. Adam and Eve missed the mark of God's holiness by sinning, that is, transgressing, the law of God (1

John 3:4). As a result, mankind would age and die: a promise God had warned Adam and Eve about when He gave them His law. Metal rusts, wood rots, pathogens wreak havoc, and life under the sun (that is, without God's intervening grace) is vanity.[26] The underlying fruit of all humanist endeavors is hopelessness and despair, which is, sadly, what characterizes many ailing nations today.

THE KING JESUS GOSPEL

Many Christians, it seems to me, have a reductionist view of the gospel. What do I mean? A truncated, reductionist view of the gospel emphasizes only *one* aspect of the King Jesus gospel. Adherents to this particular brand of Christianity tend to reduce the gospel down to 'Jesus died for me so I can get out of hell and go to heaven.' They elevate the 'spiritual' world and reduce the importance of the 'material' world. This type of thinking makes Jesus a personal Lord and Savior and *only* a personal Lord and Savior. Yes, Jesus died for your sins against God. Yes, you were buried with Christ, and also raised with Christ. You are, in fact, justified by faith alone. These are massively important basics to the Christian gospel. But that's not all!

Jesus is Lord of the universe, which is why I call it the King Jesus gospel. The 'gospel' simply means 'good news.' It is the royal announcement of the inauguration of the kingdom of God on earth as it is in heaven. This announcement is based on the work of Christ who was born of the virgin, Mary, and lived a perfect life. He died and was buried. He was raised three days later. After spending post-resurrection time with his disciples, he ascended to heaven in fulfillment of Daniel 7:13-14 in order to sit on the throne at the right hand of God our Father. The terms and conditions of His newly established covenant treaty are now being enforced in the world for the healing of the nations. So much for the gospel being reduced to 'Jesus died for me'!

---

26 See the book of Ecclesiastes.

The gospel of the Kingdom that Christ established two thousand years ago is an entire *political* ('Jesus is Lord') and *economic* (e.g., 'Thou shalt not steal') ordering of life that infiltrates and expands throughout the world in the self-sacrificial, Holy Spirit empowered, missionary activity of the Church. This Kingdom is *comprehensive* because sin is comprehensive. It is the all-encompassing authority of heaven taking full responsibility for sin (Jesus is our substitute) in order to reclaim men, women, and children for the Kingdom purpose of loving, serving, and obeying God in every single area of life so that the nations can experience *true*, gospel healing. In all His thinking and doing, Jesus of Nazareth entered into the world to proclaim and enact the kingdom of heaven because it is the kingdom of heaven that heals men, nations, and institutions. Our journey in understanding health starts here.

When we have a comprehensive gospel, as opposed to a truncated gospel, we're able to see the larger point of the gospel Jesus preached, which was centered on the imminent coming of the kingdom of God (Mk. 1:15). A truncated gospel only emphasizes something like the doctrine of justification by faith alone—a good and true and necessary *component* of the gospel. A truncated gospel might only emphasize the issue of adoption—a good and true and necessary component as well. But we must not be reductionistic with our definition of the gospel. We must see the totality of the gospel as being that which Jesus emphasized, namely, the kingdom of heaven coming to the earth in the person and work of Jesus. This comprehensive Kingdom message was at the center of Jesus's teaching and, lest we forget, all of Jesus's *actions* were centered on demonstrating this kingdom.

Think about it. Jesus preached about the ever-growing nature of the Kingdom (see Matt. 13). But He didn't just preach it, He enacted it. His 'faith' was one of theology lived-out. He healed the blind. The lame could walk. The sick were given their health back. The lepers were no longer leprous. The dead were resuscitated. Jesus didn't come to bring a doctrine-only gospel, one which has all the right dogma without any real-time, historical implications. He brought a full gospel, an across-the-board, all-of-life gospel which touched people's *physiological* lives as much as their *spiritual* lives. In other words, His actions were lined up with His preaching and when the Kingdom comes, that's just what happens to the natural world: it is *healed* (see Ezekiel 47:8ff; cf. Revelation 22:2).

While in prison, John the Baptist sent for clarification about his cousin's ministry, wanting to know if Jesus was the expected one. What did Jesus say to John's messengers? *"Go and report to John what you hear and see: the blind receive sight and the lame walk, the lepers are cleansed and the deaf hear, the dead are raised up, and the poor have the gospel preached to them. And blessed is he who does not take offense at me"* (Matt. 11:4-6). Why would Jesus add this part about 'blessed is he who does not take offense at me'? Why would that matter? I submit to you that it mattered because *John wasn't getting out of prison.* In fact, Jesus quotes from Isaiah in several places but fails to include the part about the prisoners being set free. Why? Because *John wasn't going to go free.* On top of this, the in-breaking Kingdom wasn't going to look like that which most had expected. Most first century Jews had anticipated immediate reprieve from Roman rule and occupation, coupled with an assertion of Jewish sovereignty as a nation (Acts 1:6). But Jesus had a bigger vision for the Kingdom, one which included health and wellness for those who suffered, and judgment for those who had done the infliction. 'Don't take offense,' Jesus said, because what Jesus was doing was far bigger than nationalistic aspirations. Jesus brought healing, and the healing would come through fiery judgment. The sickness of oppression ceases when the balm of the Kingdom is applied. The outcasts are brought near. Everything *changes.*

So, the gospel, then, is centered on King Jesus, uniquely tied to the ushering in of the kingdom of God (the new heavens and new earth), and with it comes a world-shaking paradigm for revival and reformation and healing. The reason we want a far-reaching gospel is because we have an all-encompassing Kingdom to deal with every problem we may encounter. Yes, we've been saved from Satan's ferocious grip. We've been rescued from our sins, past, present, and future. We've been set free from the curse of the law so we can now obey the law. All of these are necessary components and aspects of the gospel and what it does. There is, however, one more aspect to consider in the King Jesus gospel.

THE DOMINION MANDATE

When Christ died for you, you died with Him. The wages of sin is death (Rom. 3:23), and this is one paycheck no one will miss. Death reaches all men, and either Christ is your death and you die with Him, or you will die alone and face the consequence of hell: an eternal, conscious torment. But die you must; and die you will. The good news of the gospel is that it comes along and gives you a death: *Christ's* death. In this judicial act, your sins are forgiven fully and finally, and not only did you *die* with Christ, you were *buried* with Christ, and thus *raised* with Christ (Rom. 6:4; Eph. 2:6; Col. 3:1). The Spirit is a down payment for future resurrection promises (Eph. 1:13). You are now dead to the law's consequence, and alive to the law's provision. In Christ you are now a new creation (2 Cor. 5:17). But we can't stop there.

We were bought with a price and therefore, we're supposed to glorify God with our bodies (1 Cor. 6:20). We are 'fearfully' and 'wonderfully made,' so honor the King with your life (Ps. 139:14). Yes, Christ died for our sin. But Christ was also raised, and part of the raising is taking our fearfully and wonderfully made bodies and glorifying God by carry out the dominion mandate (Gen. 1:26-28). Salvation, in the fullest extent, means not just the salvation of your soul for heaven, but the redemption of your physical bodies so that we are properly suited for obedience to the dominion covenant. Adam had failed to carry out his calling. Christ, who is King Adam II, has brought us into Himself so that we may continue that calling to work and keep the garden-world. "All things belong to you" (1 Cor. 3:21), and I take this to mean that the world is now at our fingertips. In Christ, you are raised to do work for the Kingdom with joy and peace and righteousness. In Christ, you are to be healthy, happy, and holy.

What I'm suggesting is that in Christ, the world and everything therein is *ours for the taking*. This includes health and natural medicine. In Christ, we are restored and hereby ordered to carry out the commands of Christ in the world. And what are the plans? The obedience of the nations:

> The scepter shall not depart from Judah [Christ],
> Nor the ruler's staff from between his feet,
> Until Shiloh comes,
> And to him shall be the obedience of
> the peoples. (Genesis 49:10)

The New Testament counterpart is the Great Commission:

> And Jesus came up and spoke to them, saying, "All authority has been given to Me in heaven and on earth. Go therefore and make disciples of all the nations, baptizing them in the name of the Father and the Son and the Holy Spirit, teaching them to observe all that I commanded you; and lo, I am with you always, even to the end of the age." (Matthew 28:18-20)

As we like to say at Cross & Crown Church, *all of Christ, for all of life*. We have an all-encompassing gospel because sin is a far-reaching problem. It is good news because there is finally a solution to man's sin and the consequence of man's sin. It is good news because Christ the King is a good and faithful King. And our job is to refrain from trying to truncate and dismiss this gospel. We need the King Jesus gospel because salvation is not an 'other world only' type of thing; it is a 'this world' type of thing. We are saved *from* sin and death *for* the purpose of healing the nations. It's inescapable!

A GOSPEL PARADIGM FOR THE WORLD

Changing the world doesn't happen by adopting humanism and other God-hating tactics. In order to build the family business (the Kingdom) further into the world, we're going to have to see our work in the following paradigm:

1. **God's plan for change always begins from the inside out.** The root problem with man is his heart, so God gives grace on the inside which then spills over to the outside. Change, renovation, and maturity starts inside of you.
2. **Godly reformation always starts locally from the bottom up.** Nations are made of individuals. Win the individuals and you win the nation.
3. **Healing for the nations requires a comprehensive faith for all of life, including our vision of health and longevity.** It is not good enough to win doctrinal arguments. We must apply the gospel's comprehensiveness to every area of life.
4. **Top-down tyranny accomplishes nothing, which means we must exercise servanthood dominion.** Salvation by law never works. It can't work. External sanctification in the world is only going to come about through humble people serving King Jesus each and every day.

Jesus gained an incredible audience for the Kingdom by simply meeting people's everyday needs. Whether it was issues of social justice, sickness, or death, Jesus met the need. He did not bring people into a secret religion. He did not bring people into an escapist religion, either. He preached the real-time kingdom of heaven which was breaking into the first century through His own actions. He demonstrated the healing of the kingdom by healing people's physical bodies—the mark of a true physician. This was a *wholistic* gospel for the *whole* of man's being, physical *and* spiritual. Christ can save your soul and He can heal your body. He didn't shy away from this truth. His kingdom reaches into all the places that sin has gone, including your fight against disease and sickness.

Instead of being defiled and polluted, Jesus practiced a reverse holiness. Rather than being touched by an unclean man or women, and thus becoming defiled according to the Israelite holiness code, Jesus 'polluted' and 'defiled' the sick with His holiness. He didn't get sick or defiled, He brought healing. He was the cure. It was a reverse 'defilement': Jesus granted healing; He didn't get sick or polluted. And what I find absolutely remarkable is the fact that if you have the cure of Christ, you are immediately qualified to dispense the cure. No classes, no diplomas. The only qualification for the school of Christ is to be *in* the school of Christ. When you're in Christ, you're a healer. You have divine access to the Great Physician and you better believe that His desire is to heal the nations, starting with you. In Christ, the blueprints are ours!

CONCLUSION

As we journey further into this topic, we need to have these ideas in place. You need to know that in Christ, you are a prophet, priest, and king. You are called to labor for the Kingdom, and part of that labor includes the promotion of natural health and healing. The Church is the priesthood of *all* believers, which is this extraordinary decentralization of authority and power for the purposes of advancing this gospel of wholeness and holiness. There is no secret sauce, nor a secret elite who ultimately controls health and wellness. The MDs aren't kings. The pharmaceutical companies aren't deities to whom we must acquiesce. The philosopher-kings aren't sovereign, Jesus is sovereign. All of it is Christ's, and in Him, it belongs to you, too.

We are in desperate need of the King Jesus gospel because the world is in desperate need. We are chronically sick, infested with cancer, and the current allopathic experiment with chemicals and neurotoxins just isn't working. There are major problems, but we have answers: after all, we have the kingdom of God and the created order at our disposal. We have the King Jesus gospel. Humanism is the religion of the day and it exerts an ever-expanding intrusion on our liberties, especially when it comes to freedom in health and medicine. We need to know its philosophies so we can beat its philosophies. *You can't beat something with nothing.*

TEN THINGS FROM CHAPTER ONE

1) The longest running skirmish in history is the battle between humanism and Christianity.

2) God created man in His image, and this image bearing is a vocational calling to spread the holiness and righteousness of God into every area of life.

3) Instead of being God's holy subordinates working for God and his Kingdom plan for the world, Adam and Eve swapped their image bearing responsibilities for a life of selfish ambition and self-determination.

4) Jesus is the Lord of the universe, which is why I call it the 'King Jesus gospel'.

5) The gospel of the Kingdom that Christ established two thousand years ago is an entire *political* ('Jesus is Lord') and *economic* (e.g., 'Thou shalt not steal') ordering of life that infiltrates and expands throughout the world in the self-sacrificial, Holy Spirit empowered, missionary activity of the Church.

6) The reason we want a far-reaching gospel is because we have an all-encompassing Kingdom to deal with every problem we may encounter.

7) We were bought with a price and therefore, we're supposed to glorify God with our bodies (1 Cor. 6:20). We are 'fearfully' and 'wonderfully made,' so honor the King with your life (Ps. 139:14).

8) We need the King Jesus gospel because salvation is not an 'other world only' type of thing; it is a 'this world' type of thing. We are saved *from* sin and death *for* the purpose of healing the nations.

9) Jesus gained an incredible audience for the Kingdom by simply meeting people's everyday needs.

10) We are in desperate need of the King Jesus gospel because the world is in desperate need. We are chronically sick, infested with cancer, and the current allopathic experiment with chemicals and neurotoxins just isn't working.

There are major problems, but we have answers: after all, we have the kingdom of God.

CHAPTER TWO

Healing The Nations

"The leaves of the tree were for the healing of the nations."
Revelation 22:2

God desires to heal the nations. This is the purpose of the King Jesus gospel. When Jesus stooped low to live among us, He did so in order to be established as the Lord of the universe. His incarnation (taking on flesh) was the decisive moment when our world was forever changed. God becoming man was indeed the remarkable event which altered the course of human history. Jesus lived, died, was raised, and was enthroned, and all of it happened so that heaven could now come to the earth in a fresh way. This new heavens and new earth established by Christ became a new working reality, which is why Jesus told us to pray, "Your kingdom come; Your will be done on earth, as it is in heaven" (Matt. 6:10).

This prayer, what we call the Lord's Prayer, is simple enough for a young child to memorize, yet powerful enough for nations to be changed. When we ask for the will and kingdom of God to become a tangible reality here on this planet, do we recognize the implications of what it is we are saying? Do we really believe God intends to answer this prayer? Do we consider healing as part and parcel to the request? Far too many Christians repeat this prayer with rote and vigor and yet do not consider the consequences of such ideas. God's kingdom on earth as it is heaven? God's will on earth as it is in heaven? Absolutely. All of heaven thrown down on all the earth.

Indeed, God does desire to heal the nations, as this was his intention all along. Sin had given man and the world the only paycheck it knows, that being death. Consequently, the King Jesus gospel came to undo the damage. As we saw in the last chapter, this far-reaching problem was given an even further reaching solution. The rule and reign of Christ over the world has the intention of redeeming and rescuing and healing the world—nations and people groups included. When Jesus sat down next to the Father after accomplishing His gospel-mission, He leaned over to the Father and asked, "The nations, please?"[27] The Father gave them to the Son as an inheritance for His labor and work on the earth.

In light of this, we need to connect this idea of healing the nations to man and his purpose.

WHAT IS MAN?

What is man? The question is entirely worth asking, albeit the question is often ignored. Humanism, as we learned in the last chapter, has its alleged answers. Man is whatever *he* decides. His being is what *he* says it is. He is self-determined, not God-determined. He is selfish, not self-less. Even so, do Christians have an answer to the question? Do *you* have an answer? If not, why not? If so, does it include biblical categories? Does it share the presuppositions of humanism?

If someone walked up to you and said, "What is man?" what would you say? Is he a created being made in the image of God? Or is he an evolved machine suitable for chemical experimenta-

---

27   Psalm 2:8 – "Ask of Me, and I will give you the nations for your inheritance, and the ends of the earth for your possession."

tion? Does he exist in a particular historical context for a God-determined purpose? Or, is he the product of time and chance imposed upon evolutionary matter? How we answer these questions determines how we approach health and wellness, and it will certainly determine whether or not a nation can experience the healing and blessing of the King Jesus gospel.

R.J. Rushdoony answered this question rather brilliantly in this way:

> God's definition of man in Jesus Christ means that man is recreated in God's image by the atoning work of Jesus Christ and is given a specific task in history. Progress is ensured and historical development opened up by means of God's defining and redemptive act. The unregenerate seek to end history: Marx's ideal order is a static, unchanging realm, and the same is true of the dream-orders of anarchists and Pragmatists. God's creation and recreation inaugurate history: man is given an objective and a purpose. The world is to be subjected to man; for this goal to be realized, man must first subject himself to God.[28]

The point that Rushdoony makes is that the gospel saves us *from* sin and *to* the kingdom of Christ. If nations are going to receive the healing the gospel gives them, they are going to have to decide to reclaim this vision of God and God's plan for man. Man is not to try and escape the world, nor is he to try and make it into his image through coercion, domination, or the exertion of power over others. Man is *not* sovereign. To truly experience healing in all senses of the word, we need to know that "man must first subject himself to God." It does no good to go it alone. It also does no good to entrust the world to money hoarding bureaucrats and government-backed pharmaceutical companies. Each of us must decide to stop relying on others to do our thinking and healing. We must exhibit self-control under the calling we have to serve God and each other,

---

28 Rousas John Rushdoony, *Revolt against Maturity: A Biblical Psychology of Man* (Vallecito, CA: Ross House Books, 1987), 146.

promoting healing and peace at every turn. What is man? Here is my answer: *God's creation* (not evolved) *designed* (there *are* blueprints) *to extend the kingdom of Christ* (not the kingdoms of men) *into every realm* (literally everything). Healing can happen no other way.

SELF-GOVERNMENT

The most basic form of all government is self-government. Made in the image of God, man is to govern himself in obedience to Christ so that he can accomplish the task just mentioned. In view of the fact that sin is a palpable reality, God has sent us the Holy Spirit to aid in the self-governing. The Bible gives us helpful clarity on what the Spirit does in our lives. *"[T]he fruit of the Spirit is love, joy, peace, patience, gentleness, goodness, faith, meekness, and self-control"* (Gal. 5:22-23a). When we focus our activities and calling on the work of the Holy Spirit, we will have love and joy, peace and patience. We will exhibit gentleness with others. We will be people marked by goodness and faith in God. Meekness and self-control will rule our hearts and thus the entirety our lives.

This principle of self-government works itself out in a variety of ways, not least the personal lusts and sins we ought to put to death. Self-government means that temptation is successfully resisted. Our minds are renewed. We exhibit patience towards others. Self-control means that we don't gorge ourselves on ice cream and donuts. *Self*-control means self-*control*, whether we're talking about food choices, medicinal choices, or personal sins. As such, we need to see the gospel as the very apparatus God has chosen to restore man back to his calling; and having the Holy Spirit inside of you is the way God has chosen to see to it that you mature spiritually and physically. In Christ you are given a great gift, the gift of self-government.

Self-government exists to reflect the self-government of God. God is not double-minded; therefore, we should not be double-minded. God is not a glutton; therefore, we should not be a glutton. God is the author and sustainer of life; therefore, we should live in accordance to His blueprints, promoting health and vitality at every turn. The principle of self-government is commensurate to our need to rid ourselves of selfishness and pride. When we are submitted to Christ, we are self-governed. When we are submitted to tyrants, we become slaves. To be self-governed in every area of life is to be ruled by Christ and his Holy Spirit, and *nothing* else.

The Bible lays out blueprints for government in four particular areas: 1) Self; 2) Family; 3) Church; and 4) Civil. Each arena has its own particular calling, purpose, and jurisdiction. Without proper self-government, none of the other areas will flourish. Fathers or mothers who lack self-control will destroy the family. Men or women who lack meekness in character will bring reproach on our civil government by longing for more political power and control. Churches lacking leaders and/or constituents who exhibit self-government will be deemed hypocritical as they indulge themselves on whatever suits them in the moment. Self-government, as you can see, is really the pivot on which every other area of life turns. Included in self-government is taking hold of our own health. The responsibility is ours. As the individual goes, so goes the family. As the individual and family goes, so goes the Church. As the Church goes, so goes the nation. The implications are self-evident.

THE WHOLE CHRIST

In the next chapter we will look at the history of medicine here in America, but for now I simply want to do a quick bible study in hopes that it will set the stage for the second half of the book. When we consider the fact that Christianity has only one rival worldview (humanism), we find that we need to truly know what we believe in order to combat it. I want us to have a wholistic view of health and medicine, but before we develop that, we need a wholistic view of the Great Physician. What does Jesus offer us? Why does He matter when it comes to the healing of the nations? These are great questions that require precise answers.

In the book of Colossians there is a Greek word that is used four times and it is a word that has colossal repercussions. The word is *arche* (pronounced 'ar-khay') and it means 'beginning' or 'origin.' Depending on the context, it can refer to a person that commences or begins something that has many implications which follow. In theological and political language, it speaks of someone having supremacy or priority as a ruler. Let's look at the verses in question.

> For by Him all things were created that are in heaven and that are in earth, visible and invisible, whether they are thrones, or dominions, or principalities, or powers. All things were created by Him and for Him.
>
> –Colossians 1:16

> He is the head of the body, the church. He is the beginning, the firstborn from the dead, so that in all things He may have the preeminence.
>
> –Colossians 1:18

> And you are complete in Him, who is the head of all authority and power.
>
> –Colossians 2:10

> And having disarmed authorities and powers, He made a show of them openly, triumphing over them by the cross.
>
> –Colossians 2:15

The texts here illustrate the supremacy and incomparability of Christ. He is the foundation and ruler of all. Being the *arche*, He is the integration point of all things. Everything was created to serve Christ, including the mitochondria in your cells. Your mind was created to use dopamine and serotonin in order to think in terms of righteousness and justice. Your heart was created in order to pump blood and oxygen to the cells in the rest of your body so you would have the energy to serve your neighbor. Your feet were created in order to run and not be weary, walk and not faint (Isaiah

40:31). The billions and billions of strands of information stored in your DNA are there because Christ was the firstborn from the dead. The entirety of your existence is predicated on Christ being the *arche*.

Everything about you exists to serve the living God. *Everything.* Wholistic healing exists because Christ is the whole—the *arche*—the Person who holds it all together. Every molecule and every atom—all of it in your body swirling round and round each and every day—is there because Jesus *put it there.* Talk about fearfully and wonderfully made! We don't fully understand the science behind how our bodies work, but what we do know ought to leave us speechless at the majesty of God.

HEALING THE NATIONS

Jesus Christ died to heal the nations.[29] His creation suffers because of sin, but His creation does not *have* to suffer. When we turn to Christ through the vehicle of repentance and faith (both gifts from God), we begin a journey of healing. Theologians call this 'sanctification.' We are 'holy', that is, 'set apart.' Christ declares us 'not guilty' and we are free from the condemnation of sin. This wonderful King Jesus gospel outlined in the previous chapter is the starting part. Christ the *arche* is the one who sets nations on the path towards healing. He's the one who forgives sin and removes curses. He's the covenant agent who administers blessing and curses, depending on obedience and disobedience (Deuteronomy 28; Leviticus 26). When men and women and institutions are faithful to Christ, the land is healed (2 Chronicles 7:14). In other words, the nations can be healed but only as long as they ditch the humanist paradigm and by repentance, turn towards obedience to King Jesus.

Consider the following texts:

29　See Genesis 12:3; Psalm 2:8; Isaiah 19:21-25; Matthew 28:18; John 11:51-52; and Revelation 22:2.

For I will restore health to you, and I will heal you of your wounds, says the Lord.

-Jeremiah 30:17

The Lord will make pestilence cling to you until it has consumed you from the land, which you are going to possess. The Lord will strike you with a wasting disease, with a fever, with an inflammation, with an extreme heat, with the sword, with blight, and with mildew, and they shall pursue you until you perish.

-Deut. 28:21-22

If you are not careful to observe all the words of this law that are written in this book so that you may fear this glorious and fearful name, the Lord your God, then the Lord will bring extraordinary plagues on you and your descendants, even great long-lasting plagues, and severe and long-lasting sicknesses.

-Deut. 28:58-59

You shall serve the Lord your God, and He shall bless your bread and your water, and I will remove sickness from your midst.

-Exodus 23:25

Over and over again, the Bible illustrates for us the blessings for obedience and curses for disobedience. God says several times in Deuteronomy 28, 'Listen, if you obey Me, you're going to see a lot of blessing. Economic productivity and leadership among the nations will come your way. Your health will be great. You will have plenty of food. Things will go well.' But the opposite is true, too. If nations do not respect the covenant and trample on the blessings that God has already given them, inflammation (Deut. 28:22) and chronic illness (Deut. 28:59) will be the result. The land will not yield crops, the soil will be depleted, and thus proper nutrition will be in short supply.

At this point it might seem unbelievable to you that the Bible actual talks in this manner. I get it. It's not something that's normally preached from the pulpits. Regardless, it *is* in the Bible and we cannot ignore it. We *should* not ignore it. The fact of the matter is, God's plan for healing the nations cannot be detached from the nation's faithfulness or lack thereof.

To clarify, this is *not* a prosperity gospel, which is a reductionistic view of faith and works and the law of God. In the prosperity gospel world, what is often called the 'name it and claim it' theology, your level of faith might get you a new *BMW* or *Mercedes*. This is not how the gospel works, nor is it how God's covenant works. When men and women are faithful to God demonstrating obedience by occupying their calling and doing business (Luke 19:13), God works to confirm and establish that obedience in a myriad of ways.

Think of it like this. The book of Proverbs says repeatedly that if you do X, then Y and Z will happen. Does it always happen this way? No. But *usually* it will because there's a level of predictability based on the wisdom of God, which tells us how things will go— generally speaking—if we accomplish X. These proverbs are called truisms. They are general truths that generally apply because life in God's world has some level of general predictability. For example, if you eat nothing but McDonald's for every meal, every single day, we can safely conclude based on general principles that you're probably going to feel terrible. Obedience to God's covenant works this way in the home and in nations.

When we value self-government and seek to steward our bodies and property well, blessings fall in place. When we value the family (the 'least of these' like children who are murdered in the womb), blessings follow. When we value justice, and so on, blessings come to us.

When a nation values and prioritizes self-government, family government, church government, and civil government all in accordance to the word of God, the nation will find itself on the path to healing.

NATIONS THAT NEED HEALING

From where I stand the Western world is in serious trouble. These ailing nations are turning themselves over to humanism, and its political counterpart, socialism. The results cannot be overstated. Cancer rates in the U.S. continue to rise. The American Cancer Society says that 1,806,590 *new* cases of cancer will come about in 2020.[30] According to the Center for Disease Control, 1 in 59 children has autism, and this continues to spiral out of control with no end in sight.[31] Each year the United States government goes further and further into debt with unfunded liabilities and a massive defense budget that dwarfs the next seven countries combined.[32] Abortion on demand continues unabated with more and more ways to kill your child coming to a store near you in the form of pills and other abortifacients. The hot topic right now is mandatory vaccination, with several states considering these draconian laws. Informed consent and medical freedom are being tossed in the trash can -- after all, the state knows best, right? This won't stop, either. Vaccines and their booster counterparts are being developed to 'serve' the elderly. Womb to tomb vaccination is on the horizon, mark my words. We have more access to healthcare, more drugs and ostensible treatment plans, yet we're the sickest we've ever been. Perhaps someone should blow the whistle?

It doesn't take a rocket scientist to figure out that the reason Big Pharma and the bloated federal government has taken so much control is because we have become amenable to their demands. We have replaced God with the state. We have replaced truth with propaganda and marketing persuasion ("If you're experiencing

---

30 American Cancer Society. *Cancer Facts & Figures 2020.* (Atlanta, GA: American Cancer Society; 2020). For more information: https://www. cancer.org/research/cancer-facts-statistics/all-cancer-facts-figures/cancer-facts-figures-2020.html

31 https://www.cdc.gov/ncbddd/autism/data.html (accessed January 30, 2020).

32 https://www.nationalpriorities.org/campaigns/us-military-spending-vs-world (accessed February 7, 2020).

_____, ask your doctor about _____"). Instead of critical thinking, research, and self-learning, we have been given a dose of group think. The most egregious thing, perhaps, lies in the fact that we have traded our freedom for security, and we're about to lose both, despite what the Nuremberg Code says. We have replaced self-reliance with dependency as the nanny-state government controls everything from birth to death. Nations aren't healed when they sell themselves out to profits and false gods.

I share this because this is what happens when a nation walks away from the Lord Jesus Christ. This is what happens when self-government breaks down. The family is left in ruins, after all, Hillary Clinton can say, "They're _our_ children." Government encroachment on every area of life is not a blessing, but a curse. Nations that opt for the humanist version of life are nations that will be squelched and irrelevant to history. Rome was too big for its own britches, and America is looking to write the sequel.

I teach and preach across the globe and my recent trips to Zambia have proven to me that so-called third world countries are riding on the coattails of our Western debauchery. Thanks to the United Nations and other God-hating institutions, nations like Zambia, Congo, and other places, are all being enticed by the Western humanist model. These collectivist institutions wave the almighty American dollar in front of the faces of third world countries but want more and more control of the politics of those countries in return. You better believe that the United Nations are evangelists of the global collective trying to spread the so-called 'good news' of vaccination, chemical experimentation, abortion, and sodomy.

The humanist utopia is total power and total manipulation in order to get total control. This is why the nations need the gospel and why the nations need to be healed. They won't be healed by domination and intimidation. Nations like America won't find healing in the CDC. A nation full of hospitals, labs, cancer clinics, and dialysis centers is not evidence of a healthy culture, but a culture under judgment. These 'religious shrines' are proof that the entire culture has submitted itself to another god of the body. Instead of trusting Christ and taking control of your health via the things outlined in the next few chapters, humanist nations worship and serve the creation, not the Creator (Romans 1:18ff). They are ailing because their particular theocracy has a false god calling the shots.

CONCLUSION

Just as faith is not to be controlled by clergy, so medicine and health is not to be controlled by doctors. Pastors and doctors are both to fulfill their role in the service of the kingdom. But the modern, allopathic version of medicine is total control of the health of people, from abortion to vaccines, to pushing pills and medical boards. A culture that does not value life and the preservation of life is a culture bent on synthetic drugs and power. If Christ will not be the Messiah of a nation, then the state will gladly fill the void. These power paradigms are the primary obstacles and culprits which leave nations sick and impoverished.

You might ask as we close out part one of the book, "Why bother with health and healing the nations? Why does any of this matter?" Let me reiterate. The vision of the King Jesus gospel is the total healing of the nations. Healing the nations presupposes sickness, and we have plenty of that to go around, both politically, socially, economically, medically, and spiritually. We have bribery in politics, injustice in the court system, inflation thanks to the Federal Reserve, abortion on demand, parental loss of freedom, and the list gets longer and longer. Yet, God has given us everything we need for life and godliness (2 Peter 1:3). We are not evolved, mechanistic goo that somehow crawled out of the pond only to grow two legs and two eyes. How long that took, no one knows. We are not, as we'll see, lacking in chemicals—the very thing state-controlled medicine seeks to put inside of you. No one, *I repeat*, no one is sick because they lack synthetic drugs.

We are fearfully and wonderfully made creatures with bodies that are designed to function given proper nutrition and healthy rhythms of life. Part of this call to heal the nations includes both healing of the soul and the body. God can heal your soul and your body—do you believe it? This doesn't mean that God doesn't use the means of proper diet, exercise, and other medical interventions in the healing process. But we must readily admit that you can't look for healing apart from the Healer. We also acknowledge an important question: What good is it if a man gains perfect health but loses his soul? None.

What we need more than anything are self-governed Christians in healthy, God-honoring families, participating locally in biblically saturated churches, seeking economic productivity with the prophetic goal of seeking justice and offering the nation a better path forward. *Health* for all of life is a thing because *faith* for all of life is a thing. When we start to live this way, the world cannot help but notice (Deut. 4). So, what will you choose? I leave you with Deuteronomy 30:1-15.

> When all these things happen to you, the blessing and the curse, which I have set before you, and you remember them among all the nations, where the Lord your God has driven you, then you must return to the Lord your God and obey His voice according to all that I am commanding you today, you and your children, with all your heart, and with all your soul. Then the Lord your God will overturn your captivity and have compassion on you and will return and gather you from all the nations, where the Lord your God has scattered you. If any of you are driven out to the outmost parts of heaven, from there will the Lord your God gather you, and from there He will get you. The Lord your God will bring you to the land which your fathers possessed, and you shall possess it. He will prosper you and multiply you more than your fathers. The Lord your God will circumcise your heart and the heart of your descendants to love the Lord your God with all your heart and with all your soul, so that you may live. The Lord your God will put all these curses on your enemies, on them who hate you, who persecuted you. You will return and obey the voice of the Lord, and obey all His commandments which I am commanding you today. The Lord your God will make you prosper in every work of

your hand, in the offspring of your body, and in the offspring of your livestock, and in the produce of your land, for good. For the Lord will once again rejoice over you for good, just as He rejoiced over your fathers, if you obey the voice of the Lord your God, by keeping His commandments and His statutes which are written in this Book of the Law, and if you return to the Lord your God with all your heart and with all your soul.

This commandment which I am commanding you today is not hidden from you, nor is it far off. It is not in heaven, that you should say, "Who will go up for us to heaven and bring it to us, so that we may hear it and do it?" It is not beyond the sea, so that you should say, "Who shall go over the sea for us and bring it to us, so that we may hear it and do it?" But the word is very near to you, in your mouth, and in your heart, so that you may do it.

See, today I have set before you life and prosperity, and death and disaster.

TEN THINGS FROM CHAPTER TWO

1) Man is God's creature, not an evolved machine suitable for chemical experimentation.

2) In order for the nations to be healed, ther peoples must subject themselves first to God.

3) Self-government is a fruit of the Spirit and is paramount to the proper function of all other government.

4) A wholistic view of health requires the whole of Christ.

5) Jesus Christ is the *arche*, the integration point for everything created.

6) God's plan for healing the nations works within the paradigm of His blessings for obedience and curses for disobedience.

7) When a nation values and prioritizes self-government, family government, church government, and civil gov-

ernment all in accordance to the word of God, the nation
will find itself on the path to healing.

8) Ailing nations are sick nations, and this is the result of
disobedience and the god of humanism being propped
up as central.

9) If Christ will not be the Messiah of a nation, then the
state will gladly fill the void.

10) What we need more than anything are self-governed
Christians in healthy, God-honoring families, participating locally in biblically saturated churches, seeking economic productivity with the prophetic goal of seeking
justice and offering the nation a better path forward.

PART TWO

Orthopraxy & Practice

The doctor of the future will no longer treat the human frame
with drugs, but rather will cure and prevent disease with nutrition.

Thomas Edison

I don't think any words have had a fuller possession of my mind through life than Christ's putting himself in the place of the sick, the infirm, the prisoner.

Florence Nightingale

CHAPTER THREE

Health, Sickness, And Sorting Out The Mess

When Jesus heard it, He said to them, "Those who are well have no need of a physician, but those who are sick. I came not to call the righteous, but sinners to repentance."

Mark 2:17

Here is the landscape we face. We live in a fallen, sinful, ethically rebellious world being renovated by the King Jesus gospel. Analogous to this spiritual condition is pain being the body's intelligent response to sickness or injury. Disease and injury, if you will, are a culture's intelligent response that things are *bad*. The 'body' (culture) has 'pain' (outward expression of stress and sickness through economic, physical, and social dysfunction). People and nations celebrate rebellion against God and His law, and this calls for negative sanctions to bring them to repentance. What 'pain' do we experience in our culture? Bad water (e.g. Fluoride and Chlorine, which are carcinogenic), nutritionally depleted soil (and as a result, animals and crops suffer), process-laden, genetically modified (GMO) food, air quality (chem trails, exhaust, etc.), household and industrial toxins, an economic crisis with skyrocketing costs in 'healthcare,' and pharmaceutical drugs and vaccines, to name only a few.

Why are Christians no better off? They experience the same things listed above, and yet the suffering and chronic conditions continue unabated. Do they serve the Creator? Do they not know any better? What about praying for the sick? Here's the truth: God will not do *our* job. In the book of James, the brother of Jesus instructed the elders to go to the sick and anoint them, which ought to be understood to mean some sort of natural, medicinal application (James 5:14). Prayer is important, but it is rather impotent without faithful action behind it. So, we must pray, and we must act.

The reality is, health is not based on luck and chance, and it's not something completely out of our reach. It's based on simple disciplines practiced daily, compounded over time. If we are willing to exhibit a teachable spirit and explore the natural, God-given remedies outlined in this book, we will be well on our way to reversing the curse of the aforementioned quandaries.

DEFINING OUR TERMS

As we deal with the problem of sickness and develop a proper definition of health, we need to break down two key ideas so we're clear on what they mean. Both of these approaches to health have worldviews behind them, and both claim to be correct. The problem, as we'll see, is that they can't both be right. The two schools of thought are 1) Reductionist medicine (allopathy), and 2) Wholistic medicine.

Naturopathy, which represents one aspect of Wholistic medicine, consists of two words, *natura* (nature/natural), the Latin root meaning 'birth', and *pathos*, the Greek root meaning 'suffering' or 'disease.' The word Naturopathy simply refers to 'natural healing.' *Allopathy*, on the other hand, consists of two words, *allos*, the Greek word for 'different', or 'other', and *pathos*, which we just covered. This word refers to 'different healing,' as opposed to natural healing.

The word 'allopathic' was first used in the 19th century by the German physician Samuel Hahnemann. Dr. Peter Glidden explains:

> Hahnemann was a homeopathic physician (a type of Wholistic medicine), and he came up with this term to describe and separate himself and the others of his profession from the MDs of his time that espoused the use of dangerous and harmful medical treatments such as blood-letting, and the use of large doses of toxic substances, like mercury.

Glidden continues to describe the current predicament:

> Modern day MDs are not so happy with the term "allopath," and will go out of their way to try to convince you that what they do is practice "Medicine"—that they in fact are the *sole proprietors* of the entire medical field. But they are not. What they do is just ONE PIECE [sic] of the medical pie. "Allopathic" is an entirely appropriate eponym for what MDs do, and Hahnemann should be applauded for his insight.[33]

Allopathic medicine is *reductionistic* medicine. Reductionistic medicine is atheistic, presupposing that man has evolved from primordial goo. While allopathic medicine is to be thanked for advancement in surgery and emergency care, it still relies on a humanist/modern understanding of the human body, as we'll see shortly.

In the world and life view of allopathy, the body is an evolved bag of evolved chemicals suited only to be controlled, put under submission, and dominated for the purpose of so-called 'healthcare.' Allopathy *reduces* the existence and physiology of man and his body down to the physical and *only* the physical. There is no 'soul' or theistic purpose; nor is there any emotional ties to a person's general physiological makeup. Allopathy is hedonistic medicine: treat the symptoms, make the patient feel 'good,' and charge them an arm and a leg in the process. Instead of *curative* medicine, allopathy is dis-

---

33   Peter J. Glidden, *Everybody Is Sick, And I Know Why* (Peter Glidden Healthcare, 2018), 5.

ease management only (you have to keep taking the pills!). A little surgery here to remove an organ, a little chemical drug over there to suppress an unwanted symptom, and *voila!* you have allopathic medicine. Again, there is much to thank, particularly as it pertains to emergency care in traumatic situations. However, there is much, much more to lament.

Reductionistic medicine views the human body as an evolved machine with moving parts that sometimes break down. Sometimes grease needs to be added (synthetic drugs), other times the parts need to be replaced (warranties are invoked). Due to these presuppositions, the answer to disease and sickness, it is believed, must be the taking apart and segmentation of the body in order to 'heal' it. When the body is reduced down to smaller pieces, one can allegedly 'fix' whatever is wrong. There are tools to this worldview. Technologies like CT scans, MRI machines, and exploratory surgeries like colonoscopies, and so on, are all 'pieces' to dealing with certain 'parts' of the body. Ideas have consequences and when man is viewed as a puzzle instead of a painting, the resultant approach to medicine follows suit.

For example, one might be on a statin drug for cholesterol but has to get on a pain killer for the headaches caused by the drug. The pain killer destroys the liver, and now one develops other issues because the body can't filter out the bad, nor produce the bile necessary for digestion and nutrient acquisition. One drug is used to cover the consequence of the other drug, and yet another drug comes into the picture to deal with the other. And on and on we go on the merry-go-round of reductionist medicine. Instead of healing the body through proper nutrition, the body is controlled by patented, pharmaceutical drugs.

The drugs are designed to oppose the symptoms, which, as Dr. Glidden points out in his book, is how they got their names in the first place. *Anti*-biotics; *anti*-inflammatory; *anti*-depressants; *anti*-histamines; *ant*-acids, and so on. The use of synthetic drugs to control the body, much like Communism, by the way, is consistent with the presuppositions of allopathic medicine today. Speaking of Communism, allopathy stems from atheistic presuppositions which is why you get what the Bible calls *pharmakeia*, or, sorcery.[34] Medical elitism means that the money-controlling establishment controls the magical potions, dictates the vaccine schedule, and lobbies the civil magistrates to enact tyrannical laws in order to secure the market. This is also why eugenics is the natural outcome of such pagan ideas. (We'll dive more into this in Appendix B).

Back to Wholistic medicine. Standing in stark contradiction to the allopathic world is Wholism and its presuppositions of the human body. Homeopathy, Naturopathy, Acupuncture, traditional Chinese medicine, Osteopathy, Chiropractic, Craniosacral and Massage therapy, and a whole host of other approaches are all contributing factors to Wholistic medicine. Instead of the atheistic approach to medicine, Wholism has a *theistic* approach. The human body, when alive, is a simple mathematic equation: The human body = body + soul; or, if you prefer, physical + spiritual. For Christians, we believe, as evidenced in part one of this book, that man is made in the image of God and possesses inherent, eternal value that surpasses the present but still informs the present. God made man, and thus man uniquely reflects God. Wholism is obviously the more biblical approach, especially when using Christian presuppositions, because Wholistic medicine starts with God and works itself out from there.

Rather than being an evolved machine, Wholistic medicine treats the body in terms of an integrated system of interrelated functions. The body didn't evolve and thus does not lack certain chemicals only to be distributed by profit-hungry, patent-holding, pharmaceutical companies. The body has the astonishing built-in feature of self-healing. It has its own regulating system -- hence the fever and sweat. It can maintain itself given the right tools of nutrition. The human body is intricately designed by God and one the greatest features of the body is its ability to *detox* harmful substances! While we have yet to determine exactly where the physi-

---

34   Revelation 9:21 – "Nor did they repent of their murders or their magical arts [*pharmakeia*] or their sexual immorality or their thefts." Revelation 18:23 – "…For your merchants were the great men of the earth, and all nations were deceived by your sorcery [*pharmakeia*]." See also Galatians 5:20.

cal meets the spiritual, we can gain understanding by applying the Christian worldview to our view of the human body.

Dr. Glidden explains:

> This innate ability of the body to manage its own affairs is what Wholistic doctors take advantage of in formulating their treatments. The fundamental belief here is that living organisms possess inherent self-healing processes which are able to be stimulated by the correct application of the proper therapeutic agent. So, for example, instead of taking an anti-biotic which is (allopathically) designed to kill certain bacteria, a Wholistic doctor will give a treatment that stimulates the body's immune system, so that the body eliminates the bacteria through its own means. This is what is meant when Wholistic doctors say that their treatments are working "with Nature."[35]

Wholistic medicine, as I see it as a Christian theologian, works with the following presuppositions, which can only be explained with a biblical worldview, and which stand in sharp contrast to the prevailing medical establishment today:

1.   **Man is fearfully and wonderfully made** (Ps. 139:14). The word "fearfully" suggests reverence and awe. God took great reverence in creating man, the crown of his creation (see Psalm 8), but a more literal reading suggests that man is "awesomely wonderful" as a creature. Cloaked in mystery, paradox, and a level of intelligibility—we can understand it to some degree!—man is a marvelous work of God's meticulous imagination. The word for 'wonderful' suggestions privilege and distinction, as in, man is distinct among all of creation. Rather than a biological heap of disorder and chaos, man and his existence under God is truly marvelous.

---

35   Glidden, 13-14.

2. **God has given us everything we need for life and godliness** (2 Peter 1:3). In Christ we are made whole, which means our ethical rebellion can be fixed. We can be made right with God through the work of Christ. In Him we have salvation. But we would be remiss to ignore the implications of this verse. The word for life is *zoe* which speaks of the totality of the created order. It's not just 'life' in the sense of a disembodied spiritual existence in heaven. The word is about the material world, too. Christ restores us not just in our relationship to God, but to our relationship with creation. The thorns given to Adam because of his rebellion were fashioned into a crown worn by the Second Adam. Jesus took the thorns—the curse of creation—on Himself, and as a result, we can, through obedience, restore all of life through the vehicle of godliness and obedience to God's law-word. But only if we would obey the blueprints!

3. **A chronically sick culture is one under God's negative sanctions for failing to apply life-giving, life-sustaining principles and practices** (Deut. 28:14ff). Seeing that God desires to heal the nations, we need to keep in mind that His program for healing has real-time, historical feedback. God blesses and God curses, and all of it is with the aim of getting people to repent. When cultures experience the oppression of rampant sickness and disease, atheistic reductionism isn't going to bring healing. And, lest we are found to be working against God by complying with that worldview, we must quickly realize that our only hope is Christ-saturated faith. In our current cultural dilemma, we have abortion, vaccination, and toxicity in our air, water, and drugs. These are not life-giving, life-sustaining principles. Instead of utilizing the tremendous power of creation to get proper nutrition, we rely on beaker-concocted phar-

maceuticals which seek, kill, and destroy unsuspecting recipients.

4. **Health is not a secret (Gnosticism) language controlled by a mysterious healing cult.** Gnosticism is an ancient heresy the Church had to fight against. Its emphasis was on *secret* knowledge being the key to life. This abhorrent philosophy has leaked over into many different things, not least the medical establishment with redacted studies, hidden ingredients, and uninhibited, liability-free, coffer-filling commerce. Healing is not for the elites, it's for everyone, everywhere, which means we must give it back to the people, not keep it secretive.

5. **As the Great Physician, Jesus has called on the sick (the sinner) to repent and be healed, not the one who is healed (the self-righteous).** Spiritual sickness requires spiritual healing, and physical sickness requires physical healing. The problem comes in when a person is too stubborn to admit his sickness. Repentance requires humility, and humility has no room for pride. When we admit our sin, Christ heals. When we admit our lack of diligence in taking care of ourselves, we are well on our way to healing.

6. **As such, we have a calling to not only repent of our passive allowance of medical tyranny but also demystify health and healing for the nations.** We have been given the Creation mandate and dominion in the world starts with the self. Health, then, is simply a matter of responsible, informed, pro-active self-government. We simply cannot allow others to take care of our health concerns. We must put self-government back in the front seat and start doing the work (yes, work) of health and healing. You can't give someone something you don't possess. We need to return to the tradition of

passing on vital information/knowledge and skill to our children and their children's children's children. After all, 'Grandma's remedy' came from *her* mom's mom.

HOW WE GOT HERE

At this point in our journey you might be asking yourself how we got into the disheveled, reductionistic mess we're in (and it *is* a mess). The onslaught of synthetic drugs didn't just come out of nowhere: that you can count on. It came in the early 20th century, and here's the story.

In 1910 the Flexner Report came out and changed everything. Abraham Flexner was commissioned and hired by the American Medical Association and other powerful companies to assess the medical schools all throughout North America. At the time there were 155 schools. Flexner's goal was to evaluate current procedures and basically massage the data in order to get the results his bosses wanted.

Up until this report, Wholistic medicine was just medicine and natural treatments ruled the day. Not only was Wholism ever so pervasive and widely accepted, the discipleship model of education was decentralized and self-regulating, much like the free market does whenever government regulations are kept at bay.

Ty Bollinger surveys the freedom before the Flexner Report:

> The greatest advancements in medicine could be attained by virtually anyone with an inquiring mind and the means and wherewithal to achieve success, all without undue bureaucratic impediment.[36]

Any time there is a change in religious presuppositions there is a change in law. When there is a major change in law and social order, we need to follow the money. The Flexner Report is no

---

36   Ty M. Bollinger, *The Truth About Cancer* (Hay House: Carlsbad, CA, 2016), pg. 23.

different. Funded by the Rockefellers and Carnegies, they desired to utilize their experience in the oil industry to bring the entire medical 'establishment' under one, collective roof. Again, Bollinger explains it well:

> Recognizing that the American populace was already fully attuned to the idea of free-market medicine, the Rockefellers and Carnegies, who sponsored the report, knew they couldn't just come right out and say that they wanted to consolidate medicine into a unified system under their control. They had to figure out a way to convince people that medical education was in need of reform, which they did by promoting the idea that medical schools were ripping people off for private gain.[37]

What you need to know is that 1910 marked a tremendous turn in medicine and that the Flexner Report, and its financers, are to blame. In order to collectivize and socialize medicine, uniformity needed to be implemented. In order to accomplish this control, the public needed to be persuaded. Who better to persuade the masses than the rich and powerful? Abraham Flexner (and his brother Simon) were hired to travel the world, document what needed to be changed, all with the goal of taking over medicine.

As a result, the landscaped changed. The number of medical schools decreased. Accreditation stipulations increased. Students had to meet strenuous requirements and schools had to run a certain way. New legislation governed this new vision for what constituted proper 'science-based' medicine. There was a hostile takeover of Johns Hopkins-style schools which were strategically placed throughout the country. Everything changed, and it changed *fast*.[38] In a matter of years, homeopathy schools closed, herbalists were out of business, and chiropractors were labeled quacks. Apprehending the establishment meant an overhaul of law, an overhaul of education, and a smear campaign against anyone and everyone who challenged the new paradigm. The medical crusade reduced competi-

---

37 Ibid., 24.
38 Ibid., 28.

tion, centralized control through money and grants...and because of all these efforts just 100 short years ago, we have the mess we have today, with more and more government barnacles being added every year.

Bollinger summarizes:

A conspiracy between Big Oil and Big Pharma arose because these entities are basically *one and the same:* synthetic drugs were manufactured from petroleum derivatives sourced through John D. Rockefeller's Standard Oil monopoly. Rockefeller and his coconspirators would stop at nothing to maintain their grip on both fuel and pharmaceutical medicine, and they were willing to fight against all traditional therapeutics in order to accomplish this.[39]

This is how we got into the mess we're in; but we need to get out of it, and we need some strategies and definitions in order to do so.

WHAT IS HEALTH?

According to Dr. Glidden,

Health is the ability of a living organism to experience stress and remain symptom free, wherein the systems of the body exist in a natural state of harmony and equipoise [balance], each to the other.[40]

While I do believe that the definition is succinct and proper, I would adjust it slightly. Health is the ability of an image bearer to experience stress and adversity while remaining symptom-free wherein the integrated systems of the body in their God–given, created state are functioning in their proper capacity in a state of

---

39 Ibid., 35.
40 Glidden, 18.

balance, peace, and shalom. Now, this may seem like I'm splitting hairs, but the point I'm making is that the 'natural' body exists the way it does because God says it should. These integrated bodily functions are what they are because God spoke, and it was so.

On top of this theological principle is the fact that the body isn't *just* a physical system, which is what Glidden seems to imply (whether he knows it or not). The 'living organism' is both physical and immaterial, which means that we have to ensure that there is a place for emotional balance and tranquility of heart as well. 'Health' is more than just having a healthy liver and thyroid, for example. It's also having peace and joy in the Holy Spirit.

Health, then, includes proper function of the following non-exhaustive things:

1. **Neurological system:** Your cerebral spinal fluid ought to be flowing properly up and down your spine. This requires a healthy Sphenoid bone which serves as a conduit for cranial nerves in your head. You also have dura mater, which is a thick membrane that surrounds both the brain and your spinal cord. Chiropractic care, Craniosacral therapy, and other osteopathic treatments are important for your nervous system's overall health. And, on top of this, you need good gut health because your gut produces much of the serotonin and dopamine in your brain.

2. **Circulatory system:** Blood flow is essential. Your cells need oxygen and the way this happens is through the vast vehicle known as your blood. Regular movement and exercise—even if it's only 20 minutes per day—is essential to exercising your heart muscle so it can properly distribute blood to the rest of the body.

3. **Immune and Lymphatic system:** Your body needs a sewer system to flush out the bad, and having a healthy liver and gut makes it all happen. Proper nutrition, sweating (infrared saunas, exercise, etc.) will help boost these systems.

4. **Digestive system:** Your body needs healthy cells (we'll discuss this shortly) and proper nutrition is essential (see the next chapter). Food goes into your mouth, is sent to the stomach to be sorted out, and the enzymes, vitamins, nutrients, amino acids, and fatty acids interact with the bile produced by your liver (which is stored in the gallbladder) in order to filter out what the body needs in order to keep cells healthy. Eating good foods and avoiding bad foods is only one aspect of health.

5. **Emotional/Spiritual system:** You are a whole person made in the image of God and while you do have a physical body which requires proper function, your heart, soul, and mind need emotional health, too. When you grumble, worry, and give yourself over to fear and fatalism, the physical transactions happening in your brain and nervous system negatively affect your body. Your thoughts are both physical *and* metaphysical. You can't purchase thought at the store. Since you are a created being who's called to reflect God, you need to be emotionally healthy, too, and this means getting right with your Creator (see chapter one).

We don't have the time or space to get into every single anatomical function of the human body, but I would encourage you to get familiar with each of the things listed previously. You are responsible for your health and trying to remember your sixth-grade science class material just isn't going to happen. You need to be healthy to participate in the healing of the nations, so don't make excuses. Learn just how fearfully and wonderfully made you truly are!

WHAT IS SICKNESS?

If health is *resistance* to symptoms and stress, then sickness is the *inability* to resist the stress. Stress, by the way, is not necessarily the tension you feel because your schedule is too busy. Dr. Glidden points out that there is positive stress and negative stress. Positive stress, like lifting weights, makes tissues and muscles stronger. Negative stress, like EMF overload, hurts the electromagnetic growth of cells. Good stress is good, and we want to cultivate this stress each day. Bad stress, however, like weather and temperature, lack of nutrition and bad water, is something we need to avoid at all costs.

When the body doesn't have the tools needed to regenerate itself, sickness occurs. "People get depression, allergies, asthma, colitis, arthritis, cancer, etc., because they have a physiological weakness (that they either acquired at birth, or developed over time, or both—usually it is both) that was capitalized upon by the stress of life. This applies to ALL [sic] disease states."

Dr. Glidden further explains that negative stress can be broken down into three categories:

1) *Common* stressors: These are the types of stress that affect everybody differently. Examples are: weather, food, common bacteria, deadlines at work, heights.

2) *Mega* stressors: These will cause a reaction in *anyone* who is exposed to them, regardless of their susceptibility. Some examples would be: bullets fired from a gun, intense heat, exceptionally virulent microbes, and ionizing radiation.

3) *Chronic* stressors: These types of stress will wear somebody down and cause a reaction regardless of how weak/strong their systems are, but the negative effects of chronic stressors happen *after extended periods of time*. For example: If someone lives in a mold-infested house for 3 years, they *will* get sick. If someone inhales asbestos fibers 5 days a week for a few years, they *will* develop lung cancer.[41]

As you can see, living in a fallen, sin-sick world has its stressors. Symptoms only come about when stress, prolonged or not, is exacerbated and running free. The human body works to adjust itself in

---

41   Ibid., 21.

order to fight off the sickness. Things like pain, swelling, and fever are the body's natural way of resisting the bad and establishing balance in the body.

What we don't want to do is suppress what the body is doing to bring said balance. Aspirin, Tylenol, NyQuil, and other drugs mask and suppress the systems and do nothing to deal with the stress. This is what we mean by disease management. In order to 'cure' the sickness, the body needs the tools to do what it is designed to do. Refraining from masking the symptoms is only the start; equipping the body with proper tools is the rest of the story.

CELLULAR HEALTH IS GROUND ZERO

You have probably never been told this by your local allopathic medicine community, but your body is an electrical grid with many moving parts. At the microscopic level, you are a composition of trillions of cells. Your cells are made of atoms, and electrical energy is built within the cellular framework. The human body, then, is controlled primarily by electronics (physics), not chemistry.[42] In order to get healing you must make sure your cells have proper voltage. Every single cell is designed to run at about a negative 20-25 millivolts. When cells need to be repaired, the voltage increases to -50 millivolts.[43] The way we measure voltage is the pH scale (pH stands for 'potential hydrogen'). Cancer and disease flourish when the body is acidic. The body is acidic when voltage is low. When voltage is low, you're losing electrons, and this is how cells die. Health is maintained and healing takes place when cells are *remade*. This requires proper voltage.

Consider the concept of regeneration, which has both a theological meaning, and a scientific meaning. Scientifically speaking, your body regenerates itself, and does so often. Dr. Tennant explains,

---

42 Jerry Tennant, *Healing is Voltage* (Self-published, 2013), pg. 57.
43 Ibid., 111.

To reverse chronic disease we must look for the reasons that we have lost the ability to make new cells work. Making new cells requires -50 millivolts of energy, amino acids to make the inside of cells, fats to make the outside of cells, vitamins and minerals to make the metabolic processes work, oxygen, a fuel system (fats and glucose), a sewage system to get rid of waste proteins (lymphatic system), a system to protect us from infections, and a way to get rid of toxic substances.[44]

Regeneration is crucial for the body because we get well not by trying to fix bad cells but by making new ones. "We replace the rods and cones in our retina every forty-eight hours. The lining of our intestines is replaced every three days. We replace our skin every six weeks, our liver every eight weeks, our nervous system every eight months, and our bones every year."[45]

If you want to be healthy and fight off sickness, you need to think about the ways in which you can make new cells. You need raw materials in order to make them. When your voltage is -50 millivolts, the cellular pH is 7.88, and when this happens, you make new, healthy cells. When your voltage is +30 millivolts, your cellular pH is 6.48, and this is when cancer occurs. Cancer isn't some foreign substance that gets into your body from places we don't know. Cancer is simply bad cells gone rogue. What we call 'cancer' is simply the body's reaction to toxicity and dangerous pathogens being allowed to roam free.

Good, healthy cells—given the proper tools—heal themselves from pathogenic harm, keeping cancer from inexorable development. Bad, malignant cells replicate, gather their friends to form a tumor, and drain the body's energy, redirecting the nutritional supply which ought to be funneled to good cells. These rogue cells are thieves. Inside your cell membranes are electrical capacitors which, like a battery, store electrons for reproduction and health. Inside the cell is an electron storage system known as ATP/ADP.[46] This

---

44 Ibid., 17.
45 Ibid., 29.
46 ATP is adenosine triphosphate.

system makes the cell work the way it's supposed to work. When cells have the oxygen they need, "we make thirty-eight molecules of ATP from one unit of fatty acids, but when oxygen is unavailable, we only make two."[47] When cells are restricted, they cannot provide electrons to the pathways of the cells, and thus you have sickness.

If this sounds complicated to you, don't worry. The main thing to understand here is that proper voltage in the body, which is linked to proper nutrition, makes sure the body has the tools that it needs. Sickness means the tools aren't readily available.

Pharmacist Ben Fuchs:

> A cell is a multifunctional, miniaturized, throbbing dynamo that the microbiologist Guy Brown called a "vast teeming metropolis." Cells extract nutrients from food, conduct electrical energy for a heartbeat, and detoxify poisons like pharmaceutical and food additives. Cells deliver oxygen, fight bacteria, and build bone and connective tissue. All this is occurring at an infinitesimally tiny scale. In fact, every single function of the human body must occur in a vast number of cells before we can know about it. Likewise, diseases must occur at the level of a vast number of cells before we recognize that we're sick... Behind all disease is always a group of cells that, through starvation, suffocation and toxification, no longer have the vim and vigor to do their business. All disease is cell disease.

Back to cancer for just a moment. Cancer itself isn't the bacteria, but the terrain. Bacteria in the body is normal—we have millions of such things. Not all bacteria are bad! "Rather than bacteria being the cause of human ailments…it's the *terrain* on which bacteria gains a foothold that determines whether or not a person gets sick."[48] Germs and bacteria in and of themselves are harmless

---

47 Tennant, 120.
48 Bollinger, 14.

to *healthy* cells. It's the environment that becomes the problem and fosters a place for disease to thrive.

> Your immune system, believe it or not, technically operates as a type of backup when your internal ecological terrain fails to fend off germs as a first line of defense. Cell tissue then becomes diseased, attracting more germs, and the immune system responds by kicking into high gear, sometimes with success and sometimes with failure. Maintaining a healthy internal terrain is your first priority, and boosting your immune system is second.[49]

When our voltage is on par and our alkalinity is in place, cancer cells and other diseases have a much harder time gaining a foothold. They simply cannot reproduce and perpetuate themselves when the body is in balance. The allopathic model of medicine insists that systems break down due to germs and bacteria and thus they treat it accordingly. Chemotherapy, for example, can cause cancer by strengthening cancer cells by turning them into stem cells which reproduce more cancer cells. By eliminating healthy cells (chemo is indiscriminately administered and can be total warfare on the body depending on how the cells react), cancer is allowed to run amuck.[50] When the environment is altogether ignored, the bacteria and germs are thus overemphasized. However, true healing begins when the body's environment is given the proper tools.

---

49 Ibid., 17.
50 According to the Journal of Clinical Oncology (2004), among the 154,971 cancer patients from both Australia and the U.S., and representing 22 different types of cancer (!), 2.3% of Australians, and 2.1% of Americans survived the chemo treatment longer than 5 years. This alone should deter everyone from going down the path towards chemotherapy!

7 CELL-BUILDING ESSENTIALS (CBE'S)

The proper tools and materials for health and vitality are found in the 7 cell-building essentials, which will occupy the next three chapters of the book. Dr. Jerry Tennant gives an apt illustration regarding the need for rebuilding cells and compares it to rebuilding a healthy home after a tornado strike. The effects of deficient nutrition (including poor absorption), he says, results in toxins, or disease-causing pathogens on human cells, to wreak havoc much like a tornado does to a home. No one rebuilds a home by solely purchasing the materials needed to repair a destroyed home. One would need to take a wholistic approach and take at least seven basic steps in order to make the home livable and healthy. This includes *preventative* medicine, too. The seven CBE's are summarized in three categories, which will make up the next three chapters.

#1 NUTRIFY—

The first CBE is *healthy nutrition*...via food and supplements that provide you with the 'Mighty 90.' You should only buy and use good materials to build a house. You should not try and use the materials found from the wreckage.

The second CBE is *healthy hydration*...via water that is filtered, oxygenated, cleansed, and fortified with Chlorine Dioxide (CD/MMS) and Dimethyl Sulfoxide (DMSO). To rebuild the house, you need access to clean water.

#2 DETOXIFY—

The third CBE is *healthy detoxification*...via improving cellular metabolism and liver, kidney, and sweating operations. To rebuild the house, you need to clean up the damage left from the tornado.

The fourth CBE is *healthy immune and lymphatic systems*...via strengthening the immune system and supporting the lymphatic system (especially for gut health). To rebuild the house, you have to have a working sewer system.

#2 ENERGIZE—

The fifth CBE is a *healthy nervous system*…via fortifying the nervous system with routine exercise, wholistic dental care, adequate sleep, and the application of electrons with electrical micro-currents and grounding. The new home needs safe and reliable electrical power lines.

The sixth CBE is *healthy blood, brain, bones, skin, circulatory and respiratory systems*…via making clean blood, developing a sharp, toxin-free brain, strong bones, vibrant skin, and good circulation and deep respiration. Your new home needs a solid HVAC system in place, both for heating and cooling.

The seventh CBE is a *healthy spiritual system*…via building upon God's foundation and strengthening your soul, what we call salvation and sanctification. Your house needs a solid foundation and there is no better foundation than the Word of God.

CONCLUSION

There's a lot to learn when it comes to health and healing, and, frankly, there's a lot we have to unlearn. The modern allopathic model of medicine has a vicious grip on unwitting participants. For the past 100 years we have been sold a bill of goods and services that has done nothing but perpetuate more disease and chronic illness. The current healthcare industry will tell you that it promotes health and healing, but this is nothing but sloganeering and smoke and mirrors. Preying on vulnerable people, manipulating them through fear tactics, all of it is done to generate billions of dollars. But are we really healthy? No. How is it we boast in our technological advancement yet here in America we are experiencing *increasing* rates of cancer and disease? We are not as healthy as we like to think. The pervasiveness of allopathic clinics sprinkled all over the place is most assuredly not a sign of health.

The mess we're in stems from bureaucratic meddling, and when you think about it, every other area of life that has such government encroachments and controls ends in the same cesspool of tyranny. Although briefly outlined previously, the Flexner Report information is readily available for further exploration and you should look into it. Make no mistake, this was the decisive turning point when the keys to the car were handed over to centralized control -- when you follow the money, you can find the movers and shakers.

It's not enough to be frustrated by the meddling. We must get back to the basics of understanding health, healing, and sickness—we must get our car back. At the molecular level, you are made up of cells—lots of them. The seven cell-building essentials are designed to take the presuppositions of Christian theology and apply them. Focusing on the ground level components to health and healing through simply, daily rhythms is the key to health.

"There shall no longer be an infant who lives only a few days nor an old man who has not filled out his days. For the child shall die a hundred years old, but the sinner being a hundred years old, shall be accursed" (Isaiah 65:20). The Bible's grand vision for the kingdom of God on earth (as it is in heaven!) is for men, women, and children to be healthy, having proper nutrients, proper detoxification, and storehouses of energy—to live a long, fruitful life with healthy cells so that we may serve love God with everything inside of us, and love our neighbor as ourselves. And now we must turn to the seven CBE's.

TEN THINGS FROM CHAPTER THREE

1) Sick bodies produce symptoms, much like sick cultures produce symptoms. Our cultural symptoms are faithfully killing us: Bad water (e.g. Fluoride and Chlorine, which are carcinogenic), nutritionally depleted soil (and as a result, animals and crops suffer), processed-laden, genetically modified (GMO) food, air quality (chem trails, exhaust, etc.), household and industrial toxins, an economic crisis with skyrocketing costs in 'healthcare.' and pharmaceutical drugs and vaccines, to name only a few.

2) The two rival models for healthcare are 1) Reductionistic/ Allopathic and 2) Wholism. Both have worldviews and presuppositions behind them, and both claim to be able to bring you healing.

3) Reductionistic medicine views the human body as an evolved machine with moving parts that sometimes break down. In order to 'heal' the machine, grease must be applied (drugs) and parts must be switched out (organ removal, chemical manipulation, etc.).

4) Wholistic medicine treats the body in terms of an integrated system of interrelated functions. The body didn't evolve and thus does not lack certain chemicals.

5) The body has the astonishing built-in feature of self-healing. It has its own regulating system, hence the fever and sweat. It can maintain itself given the right tools of nutrition. The human body is intricately designed by God and one the greatest features of the body is its ability to *detox* harmful substances!

6) In 1910 the Flexner Report came out and changed everything. Abraham Flexner was commissioned and hired by the American Medical Association and other powerful companies to assess the medical schools all throughout North America. This was the decisive moment when the landscape of healthcare changed in America.

7) Health is the ability of an image bearer to experience stress and adversity while remaining symptom-free wherein the integrated systems of the body in their God-given, created state are functioning in their proper capacity in a state of balance, peace, and shalom.

8) If health is *resistance* to symptoms and stress, then sickness is the *inability* to resist the stress. When the body doesn't have the tools needed to regenerate itself, sickness occurs.

9) Your body is an electrical grid with many moving parts. At the microscopic level, you are a composition of trillions of cells. Your cells are made of atoms, and electrical energy is built within the cellular framework. The human

body, then, is controlled primarily by electronics (physics), not chemistry.

10) The proper tools and materials for health and vitality are found in the 7 cell-building essentials.

CHAPTER FOUR

Nutrify

"Jesus said to them, 'I am the bread of life.

Whoever comes to Me shall never hunger, and however believes in Me shall never thirst'."

John 6:35

When the Lord Jesus Christ said that He was the bread of life, He was connecting the dots between the spiritual and the physical. He had just performed the miracle of feeding the five thousand and while He was quite pleased to bless the masses, His greater motivation was the revelation of His purpose in coming to the earth. The feeding pointed to something beyond what the eye could see. Jesus is bread; He is *manna*. Like the manna that had come to Israel in the wilderness many years before, here Jesus came to a spiritually lethargic, spiritually anemic people in the very same wilderness predicament in order to announce His great provision. Providentially, the word 'manna' means, 'What is this?' and Jesus answers the question. It's all about bread, but not just regular, plain old bread: it's *nourishing bread which consists of life*. They wanted manna—an uncertain provision. They needed bread—a certain provision in Jesus.

I don't believe Jesus was giving a nutrition lesson—so let me rule out that objection. He wasn't discussing the nature of cellular health and the need for the 'Mighty 90' nutrients. He was, however, making a connection between heaven and earth. Bread (food) is needed to satiate and sustain us. Remember, He had just fed a whole lot of people! But the sustenance of the physical is akin to the sustenance of the spiritual. Like bread which fills the body, so Christ fills the Christian. When we come to Christ, we never hunger. When we believe on Christ, we never thirst. He fills us. Jesus Christ claims the title of Ultimate Sustainer. He's the one who created selenium, vitamin C, and the omega-3 essential fatty acids. He *made* those things in order to point us to our need for him. When we trust Jesus, rely on Jesus, and shape our lives in accordance to Jesus's will, we experience true healing, an eternal life that does not just stamp your ticket for heaven; it stamps your ticket for today. The Bible is not a blueprint for what to do when you get to heaven, it's a blueprint for how to behave now. This means that we must be healthy, and we must acquire proper nutrition. Why? So we can serve God and neighbor.

CELL BUILDING ESSENTIAL #1: HEALTHY NUTRITION

The secret to a healthy life is developing healthy cells, and healthy cells can only be healthy to the degree that they receive the proper raw materials. Remember the tornado problem from the last chapter? When we are nutritionally *depleted*, the *absorption* of nutrients is lacking, and this results in toxins and other pathogens destroying our systems much like a tornado does to a home. The only way to rebuild is with the proper raw materials. You should only use *new* materials. You should not try and rebuild the home using the scattered, old materials found in the wreckage.

Take heed to Dr. Joel Wallach, Dr. Ma Lan, and Dr. Gerhard Schrauzer:

To achieve maximum fertility and healthy outcomes of birth-defect free pregnancies, healthful disease-free lives and maximum longevity, one must supplement with all 90 essential nutrients to warranty their optimal daily intake. You cannot depend on your food to be your sole source of macro and micronutrients. Failing to be proactive and to consume the optimal supplement program based on body weight, you will contract nutritional-deficiency diseases and spend excessive amounts of time and money on medical care and prescriptions. The secret is to give your body the raw materials, the 90 essential nutrients, rather than depend on technology to deal with diseases after they appear.[51]

Dr. Wallach describes the problem with using the old adage, 'you are what you eat', believing it to be entirely incorrect. In his mind, 'you are what you absorb'. *Proper absorption of nutrients is the key to unlocking health.* Please read that again. We simply must have healthy *absorption.* There are, however, a couple of things inhibiting nutritional absorption.

Hypochlorhydria (low stomach acid levels) and gluten intolerance are both chief suspects as it pertains to getting proper nutrition. Dr. Wallach and company explain hypochlorhydria:

The raw material for the Chief Cells, the acid-manufacturing cells of the stomach, to make hydrochloric acid is NaCl, which is salt. Stomach acid is required to keep the stomach environment sterile and free of bacteria, viruses, yeast, and fungus. Failure to keep the stomach environment at a low pH below 2.0 results in organism overgrowth, gastric fermentation, and reflux. This acidic gastric environment is also required to facilitate the absorption of vitamin B12 by activating the "intrinsic factor" that is produce by specialized cells in the stomach wall; to activate the stomach enzyme "pepsin," which in the presence of stomach acid will breakdown protein

---

51 Joel Wallach, Ma Lan, and Gerhard Schrauzer, *Epigenetics: The Death of the Genetic Theory of Disease Transmission* (Select Books: New York, NY, 2014), 370.

into amino acids, peptides, and polypeptides that facilitates absorption; and to facilitate the absorption of minerals.[52]

The second problem, gluten intolerance, is the next guilty culprit for preventing nutrient absorption.

Gluten intolerance, as a negative reaction to grain consumption, was recognized by the Egyptians and Greek physicians thousands of years ago. Gluten intolerance is not an allergy to wheat, barley, rye, or oat proteins. However, when a person is intolerant of small-grain proteins, the consumption of gluten will produce a "contact enteritis" similar to a contact dermatitis when an individual is exposed to the juices of poison ivy. No one is allergic to poison ivy; however, just about everything is intolerant of poison ivy.

The gastrointestinal damage that is produced by the gluten-contact enteritis includes celiac disease (wheat allergy that occurs concurrently with contact enteritis), diverticulitis, appendicitis, irritable bowel syndrome, inflammatory bowel syndrome, leaky gut syndrome, colitis, ulcerative colitis, Crohn's disease, gastritis, bloating, and reflux.

The gradual and progressive loss of intestinal villi as a result of contact enteritis produces a kaleidoscope of nutritional-deficiency diseases as a result of malabsorption, including infertility, birth defects (muscular dystrophy, cystic fibrosis, cerebral palsy, Down syndrome, intersex syndrome, gay behavior, etc.), colicky babies, keratosis, eczema, dermatitis, psoriasis, rosacea, asthma, fibromyalgia, lupus, sarcoidosis, diabetes, kidney failure, kidney stones, arthritis, obesity, osteoporosis, periodontal disease, dementia, heart disease, hypertension, alopecia, macular degeneration, dental problems, cataracts, nutritional secondary hyperparathyroidism, hypothyroidism, peripheral neuropathies, liver disease, constipation, diarrhea, etc.[53]

---

52 Ibid., 370.
53 Ibid., 371.

I quoted this long section to illustrate the importance of nutritional absorption. If you notice in the last paragraph of the previous quote, the laundry list of chronic illness and conditions listed arises from "the gradual and progressive loss of intestinal villi." The stomach works with the small and large intestine in order to pull out the nutrients from the food, break down the proteins, and eliminate what's left during the digestive process. Digestion, you might say, is everything, for in digestion you get the materials needed for cellular absorption. Sadly, gluten inhibits the absorption because it destroys the villi and your microbiome.

Dr. Wallach suggests[54] staying away from these ten foods:

- **Wheat**[55]
- **Barley**
- **Rye**
- **Oats, Oatmeal** (even if it says it is gluten free)[56]
- **Fried food** (nothing fried! You should boil, broil, or bake)
- **Oils**[57] (oils oxidize when they come into contact with the air (becoming rancid). Since almost all oil is continually exposed to some air from the time it is produced, the process of oxidation has begun in even the freshest oil. These oxidized oils cause inflammation and cell damage.)
- **Well done red meat** (i.e. no burned fats. Rare or medium-rare is okay! If you grill your food, try to have something between the food and the fire [like aluminum foil]

---

54 https://criticalhealthnews.com/health-news/216-dr-wallach-s-ten-bad-foods-and-good-foods (accessed February 22, 2020).

55 Organic breads ought to be considered a much safer option. Stay away from the enriched wheat flour language.

56 I don't actually agree with Dr. Wallach here. From the plant-based doctors I read, and from personal experience (I eat oatmeal every single day), oatmeal is very healthy for you. I'm sure Dr. Wallach has his reasons, but I have mine!

57 I am personally quite comfortable with organic olive oil, coconut oil, avocado oil, sesame oil, and even grape seed oil. It's the hydrogenated vegetable oil, corn oil, etc., that you need to avoid at all cost.

so the juice doesn't drip onto the flame and deposit dangerous things on the meat.)

- **Any nitrates added to meat** (i.e., deli meats; tell your butcher NO NITRATES or NITRITES!)
- **No carbonated drinks** (of any kind within one hour before, during, or one hour after meals.)
- **Skin of a baked potato** (or yam, or sweet potato; if you boil a potato, you can eat the skins.

Avoid Cancer-Causing Toxins

Much of what passes for food today is nothing but chemically concocted products that appear to be food but end up messing with your body's natural processes. 'Garbage in, garbage out' is an apt description for the little snacks, cereals, and boxed food that Americans love. The problem is, thousands and thousands of chemicals are integrated into the food supply and not only are they not adequately tested, they are altogether ignored by the FDA, which is a 'pay-to-play' organization anyway. If you want healthy nutrition, stay away from the middle of the grocery store (for the most part) and shop on the outer edges.

The following list of what to avoid comes from *The Truth About Cancer*,[58] and are things we ought to stay away from:

1. **Hydrogenated and partially hydrogenated vegetable oils**. Shelf life is everything, so manufacturers use these unhealthy oils to make the product last longer. These 'trans' fats become problematic because they are incapable of binding with oxygen, and thus they clog your cells and your body up like sludge in a pipe. Trans fats are plastic fats and when your cell membranes are coated in plastic, they can't reproduce and fight off the bad stuff, which means there's no voltage and thus cancer and disease runs rampant. "The cell membrane becomes so saturated with glucose that it begins to off-load it

---

58   Bollinger, *Truth About Cancer*, 145-152.

into fat cells. Thus people who continue to eat plastic fats get fatter and fatter."[59] When your cells are wrapped in plastic, your body responds negatively. Your brain, as Dr. Tennant illustrates, doesn't work well and becomes "prone to depression, chronic fatigue, attention deficiency, brain fog, etc."

2. **Refined sugars.** Cane sugar is a step ahead of a high-fructose corn syrup because the pancreas can still produce insulin. The problem is, refined sugars encourage rogue cells (like cancer cells) to ferment and feed the cells. Refined sugars rigorously feed bad cells. Staying away from sugar starves the enemy.

3. **Aspartame, MSG, and 'excitotoxins.'** Monosodium glutamate (MSG) and aspartame are excitotoxins, meaning that they are Trojan horse chemicals that "slip by the brain's protective defenses and latch on to neuron receptors, 'exciting' them to such a degree that they eventually die."[60] These neurotoxins are deadly. Aspartame, for example, is broken down and turned into formaldehyde, which we know is carcinogenic.

4. **GMO's and crop pesticides.** The safety and efficacy of GMO's has been a question since 1996, which is when they made their debut. Bollinger notes that there are countless animal studies that have linked their consumption to gastrointestinal disorders and immune dysfunction. GMO's and the toxins used to grow them are, to put it mildly, unsafe and altogether destructive to the body.

With chronic illnesses on the rise, and pesticides and herbicides like Roundup (glyphosate) being used on our food, it's no wonder we have the problems we have today with cancer and disease.

---

59 Tennant, *Healing is Voltage*, 113.
60 Bollinger, *Truth About Cancer*, 148.

> _**ACTION STEP**_ – If you're unsure how to move forward with eliminating these toxins from your diet, start writing down what you eat, and keep track at the end of the week. Oftentimes changing one's eating habits can be like trying to take an ice cream cone from a toddler—it just won't work without someone throwing a fit! But regular discipline and food/meal planning can aid in the process. Remember: it's about _self-government_, which is a fruit of the Holy Spirit.

What To Eat

This author eats a whole food, plant-based diet and recommends reading Dr. T. Colin Campbell's book _The China Study_[61] to learn more about the importance of whole foods for proper nutrition. This groundbreaking study has a ton of information, but learning good eating habits requires effort, so do the research! We absolute must eat 'clean,' which is to say, we have to avoid the processed junk you can purchase in a box. Food is intended to go from the ground to our stomachs, without much machinery getting in the way. Avoid the highly processed, boxed foods as well as the sugar-laden drinks and snacks that have no nutritional value. Fruits and vegetables make up a large part of this author's diet and juicing them increases nutritional intake and provides the body with a greater amount and greater density of essential minerals, vitamins, and so on.

You should be eating lots of fruit, especially organic whenever possible. Chris Wark documents a study done by Cornell University where the researchers dripped freshly extracted juice from 11 different fruits on liver cancer cells in order to see what might happen. Wark writes,

---

61   T. Colin Campbell and Thomas M. Campbell, _The China Study_ (BenBella Books: Dallas, TX, 2016).

Pineapples, pears, oranges, and peaches had very little effect on the cancer cell growth directly, but bananas and grapefruit cut the cancer cell growth by about 40 percent. Red grapes, strawberries, and apples were twice as potent as the bananas and grapefruit, but the tart fruits—cranberries and lemons— were the most powerful. Cranberries had the highest anti-cancer phenolic and antioxidant activity and cut liver cancer cell growth by 85 percent with only a third of the dose of apples and strawberries. Lemons came in a close second.[62]

Fruits and vegetables have anti-cancer properties that fight against rogue cells. Berries are especially good. "Berries are the most potent anti-cancer fruits, partly due to their ability to protect and repair damage from oxidative stress and inflammation. Blueberries contain immune-boosting and anti-cancer compounds like ellagic acid, anthocyanins, and caffeic acid."[63]

Regarding vegetables, researchers published a study in January 2009 in the journal *Food Chemistry* in which they took 34 different vegetable extracts and dripped their extracted juices on different cancer cells to see what might take place. Their conclusion? Garlic is the most powerful anti-cancer vegetable.

Garlic stopped cancer growth completely against the following tumor cell lines: breast cancer, brain cancer, lung cancer, pancreatic cancer, prostate cancer, childhood brain cancer, and stomach cancer. Leeks ran a close second and were number one against kidney cancer. But garlic and leeks weren't the only superstars: almost every vegetable from the allium and cruciferous families completely stopped growth in the various cancers tested. The allium family vegetables tested were garlic, leeks, yellow onions, and green onions. The cruciferous family veggies tested were broccoli, Brussels sprouts, cauliflower, kale, red cabbage, and curly cabbage. Spinach and beet root also scored in the top 10 against many of the cancers tested.

---

62   Chris Wark, *Chris Beat Cancer* (Hay House: Carlsbad, CA, 2016), p. 107.
63   Ibid.

Honorable mentions include asparagus, green beans, radishes, and rutabaga.[64]

If these fruits and veggies can *fight* cancer, then they are foods that can *prevent* cancer. The standard American diet, however, lacks in fruits and veggies, which is undoubtedly a contributing factor to rampant disease and cancer.

The Mighty 90

In order to recover proper nutritional absorption and keep the cellular system running on all atomic cylinders, the most important thing to do is supplement your diet with the 'Mighty 90.' The Mighty 90 are the 90 essential nutrients your body needs in order to function properly, experience healing, and stay healthy. Proper eating is only *one* aspect of healthy nutrition, and everyone *must* supplement to some degree because you cannot get what you need from food alone. The 90 essential nutrients are listed below.[65]

The 60 Essential Elements, Metals, Minerals, Trace Minerals, and Rare Earths:

- Aluminum, Arsenic
- Barium, Beryllium, Boron, Bromine
- Calcium, Carbon, Cerium, Cesium, Chloride, Chromium, Cobalt, Copper
- Dysprosium
- Erbium, Europium
- Gadolinium, Gallium, Germanium, Gold
- Hafnium, Holmium, Hydrogen
- Iodine, Iron
- Lanthanum, Lithium, Lutecium
- Magnesium, Manganese, Molybdenum
- Neodymium, Nickel, Niobium, Nitrogen

---

64   Ibid., 110-111.
65   Ibid., 371-373.

- Oxygen
- Phosphorus, Potassium, Praseodymium
- Rhenium, Rubidium
- Samarium, Scandium, Selenium, Silica, Silver, Sodium, Strontium, Sulphur
- Tantalum, Terbium, Thulium, Tin, Titanium
- Vanadium
- Ytterbium, Ytrium
- Zinc, Zirconium

The 16 Essential Vitamins for Humans and Non-human Vertebrates:

- Vitamin A
- Vitamin B1 (Thiamin)
- Vitamin B2 (Riboflavin)
- Vitamin B3 (Niacin)
- Vitamin B5 (Pantothenic acid)
- Vitamin B6 (Pyridoxine)
- Vitamin B12 (Cyanocobalamin)
- Vitamin C
- Vitamin D
- Vitamin E
- Vitamin K
- Biotin
- Choline
- Flavonoids and bioflavonoids
- Folic Acid
- Inositol

The 12 Essential Amino Acids:

- Valine
- Lysine
- Threonine
- Leucine

- Isoleucine
- Tryptophane
- Phenylalanine
- Methionine
- Histidine
- Arginine
- Taurine
- Tyrosine

The Three Essential Fatty Acids and Cholesterol:

- Linoleic Acid
- Linolenic Acid
- Arachidonic Acid
- Cholesterol

Gone are the days of blaming our illness on our parents, ancestors, and genes. New research in the field of epigenetics, including a renewed interest in Wholistic medicine, in my estimation, has snowballed into something absolutely wonderful. People are waking up to the problems of the allopathic worldview and are actively searching for answers in natural supplementation. Epigenetics, for example, is "the story of nutrition and nutritional deficiency at the enzyme, chromosomal, and gene level, and how they affect the duplication and transmission of DNA."[66] Dr. Wallach's entire life has been a study of disease, and each and every time, the diseases are a result of nutritional deficiency, not a genetic disorder. Healthy nutrition—this cannot be overstated—is absolutely, without a doubt, the foundation of physical healing and vitality. How important, for example, are vitamins? Let's take a look.

<u>Vitamins</u>

Vitamins are a collection of unrelated organic compound that are necessary as cofactors for metabolic chemical reactions within

---

66   Ibid., 222.

cells and essential for normal growth and maintenance of health. Vitamins are essential nutrients in that most cannot be manufactured in the body and many perform as coenzymes. Vitamins do not supply calories or contribute to body mass."[67] Vitamins are essential in regulating the body's metabolism. They convert carbs, fats, sugar, and proteins into the energy necessary for cellular health.

- **Vitamin A** – Essential for growth stimulation, the maintenance and function of the retina, your skin, and the intestinal mucosa. Deficiencies result in night blindness, infertility, depression, acne, depressed and suppressed immune system, birth defects, cancer, and much more.
- **Vitamin D** – Essential for calcium absorption, hormone balance, and parathyroid functions. Deficiencies result in tics, Tourette's syndrome, twitches, cramps, profuse sweating, rickets, restless leg syndrome, degenerative arthritis, and kidney stones.
- **Vitamin E** – Essential for antioxidant functions, protection of cells from oxidative inflammation, protection of red blood cells, muscular and neurological health. Deficiencies result in Alzheimer's disease, anemia, infertility, depressed immune system, cellulite, Ischemic heart disease, fibrocystic breast disease, fibromyalgia, cystic fibrosis, and muscular dystrophy (also related to selenium deficiency).
- **Vitamin K** – Essential for the liver's production of several proteins necessary for blood clotting and the distribution and deposition of calcium in the bones. Deficiencies result in extended clotting time, liver disease, osteocalcin deficiency, dysfunction of calcium absorption, osteoporosis, osteoarthritis.
- **Vitamin B** – Essential for energy production, optimal metabolism of carbohydrates, and glucose distribution. Deficiencies result in anxiety, confusion, nausea, depres-

---

67   Ibid., 373.

sion, mental confusion (dementia), congestive heart failure, fibromyalgia, paralysis, and anorexia.

- **Vitamins B1, B2, B3, B5, B6, B7, B9 and B12** – All essential for various interrelated reasons connected to neurological and organ functions in the body.
- **Vitamin C** – Essential for the production of collagen, connective tissue, cartilage, bones, teeth, blood vessel walls, capillaries, the absorption of iron. Deficiencies result in bleeding gums, loose teeth, bruising, dry skin, anorexia, poor growth, elevated cancer risk, scurvy, slow wound healing, and swollen joints.
- **Choline** – Essential for healthy cell structures related to the central nervous system. Deficiencies result in fatty liver, liver cirrhosis, kidney hemorrhage, dementia, Alzheimer's disease, and Huntington's disease.[68]

Key Nutrients

I want to highlight a few key nutrients. They are all important, but they are not all the same.

- **Calcium** – Calcium is the most abundant mineral in the human body. Nearly all the calcium in your body is found in your bones and teeth, with only a little in your blood and cellular fluid. Calcium is absorbed through the natural digestive process, specifically in the small intestine. Calcium, along with magnesium, zinc, iron, and copper, helps the body produce serotonin. If you're lacking in calcium, you can't make serotonin, which means you'll end up depressed. Its importance cannot be overstated as calcium deficiencies account for 147 diseases.[69]
- **Magnesium** – Magnesium is required in order to produce and transfer energy necessary for the body to make use of protein. It also helps with muscles and nerves as they

---

68   Ibid., 373-394.
69   Glidden, *Everybody Is Sick*, 90.

stretch and move and function. In the muscular system, calcium is the stimulator for the muscle, magnesium is the relaxer. If you lack Mg, you'll likely experience asthma, anorexia, menstrual migraines, neuromuscular problems, depression, muscular weakness, tremors, vertigo, and the calcification of small arteries.[70]

- **Selenium** – Selenium has received quite a bit of attention and rightfully so. *Se* prevents the body's fats from going rancid. It is known to improve 'genome stability' as it works on the cellular level to protect from oxidative damage. If you're looking to detox metals like mercury, selenium helps by strengthening the liver to do its job. Deficiencies in selenium are connected to infertility, miscarriage, breast cancer, muscular dystrophy, heart palpitations, anemia, HIV, fatigue, scoliosis, pancreatitis, Parkinson's disease, and Alzheimer's disease (a physician-caused disease associated with the use of statin drugs, low cholesterol intake, and consumption of free radicals). Selenium is listed here because it is an anticarcinogenic mineral, and a powerful one at that. It works to detox the bad and promote the cell's respiratory efforts at producing and promoting oxygen in the body.[71] If you're want to prevent cancer, or if you have cancer and you'd like to fight it, supplement with selenium.

Nitric Acid

The human body needs oxygen to make new cells and it needs oxygen to keep them working. Hemoglobin in the blood distributes the oxygen to the cell. In order to get the blood to the tissue, you have to have circulation. In order to have proper circulation, you have to have nitric oxide.[72] Your body naturally produces nitric oxide. You can increase your nitric oxide through special exercise

---

70   Wallach, *Epigenetics*, 452.
71   See Ibid., 467–468.
72   Tennant, *Healing is Voltage*, 523.

(CBE #5) and supplementation. Youngevity's 'CardioBeets' is one of the better sources of nitric acid.[73] Not to be confused with nitrous oxide (N2O, 'laughing gas'), nitric acid (NO) is a gas that serves as a singling molecule in every cell of the body. It causes arteries and bronchioles to expand; allows brain cells to communicate with each other; and causes immune cells to kill bacteria and cancer cells.

Humic & Fulvic Acid

"When our cells are not functioning properly and become weakened and even die, we feel this as a loss of vitality. We experience fatigue, illnesses, disease and even death. Humic and Fulvic are vitally important electrolytes to establishing and maintaining a healthy cellular membrane potential. When we receive all these nutrients, we naturally feel better and more alive. Equally important to humic and fulvic's role in nutrient activation and delivery to the cells for superior health is fulvic's ability to improve waste and toxin removal from cells and tissues by restoring cellular membrane electrical difference between inside and outside of each cell."[74]

Often called Nature's "Mineral Molecules," fulvic supplies voltage and humic provides the vitamins, minerals, and amino acids necessary to make new cells. Fulvic is golden in color whereas humic is almost black. A single molecule of humic acid can individually carry up to 60 different vital-activated minerals into our cells. Another one of fulvic's biological functions is its ability to remove heavy metals and other toxins that are stored in our fatty tissues in order to protect vital organs from these toxins. Fulvic acid acts as an escort, safely removing toxins from the body.

Moringa Oleifera

Moringa is probably the most nutritious plant on the earth. It is "God's Mighty 90!" Moringa is incredibly effective because it has 25x more iron than spinach; 15x more potassium than bananas; 4x

---

73 I am a Youngevity distributor who uses their products and *highly recommends* their products. Learn more here: https://drjasongarwood.youngevity.com
74 Ibid., 547-548.

more protein than eggs; 10x more Vitamin A than carrots; 7x more Vitamin C than oranges; and 7x more calcium than milk. Moringa Oleifera is a tree native to the Himalayas in north western India. It is an annual that can grow in tropical and subtropical areas. Known as the "Horseradish tree," moringa contains 92 different nutrients and 46 different antioxidants. This 'tree of life' is entirely usable and is a powerhouse of nutrition. You can find moringa in powder form or in capsules.

ACTION STEP – Consider using moringa in your routine. You can make smoothies with it, take it in pill form, or even grab some organic teas that contain moringa powder.

The Endocannabinoid System

You've heard of cannabidiol, right? 'CBD' oil is a hot commodity in the American economy and people are starting to realize just how helpful this stuff really is. Dr. David Allen, an experienced heart surgeon who serves as a member of the International Cannabinoid Research Society, explains: "The discovery of the endocannabinoid system (ECS) is the single most important medical/scientific discovery ever....and will save more lives than the discovery and application of the sterile surgical technique."

Discovered just thirty years ago, the ECS is a chemical communication system in your body. It is not electric, but chemical, much like our hormonal systems. The body manufactures cannabinoids (more than 80!) which perform some rather miraculous functions. The ECS is responsible for homeostasis (environmental balance and proper function) in the body. The use of CBD oil spurs on the ECS to fight against cancer, diabetes, and stroke. It is not psychoactive like THC found in the marijuana plant is.

The benefits of CBD are numerous. It is an anti-seizure and anti-epileptic oil. It helps the neurological system by decreasing anxiety and promoting chemical tranquility. While it can be used to treat various diseases, CBD oil is a helpful preventative for daily use which promotes the general health of the immune system. It is also a powerful antioxidant. Used to help treat autism, CBD has personally been beneficial to this author's family.[75]

As you can see, nutrition and nutritional absorption are foundational to cellular health and cellular health is foundational to the body's overall health. I recommend supplementation with Youngevity and a daily regimen of CBD oil.

CELL BUILDING ESSENTIAL #2: HEALTHY HYDRATION

The human body is roughly 75% water. To say that your body *needs* water is almost an understatement: your body *is* water! Healthy hydration is essential to cellular health but not all water 'sources' are created equal. In order to receive the benefits of water it needs to be filtered of contaminants, oxygenated, and routinely cleansed and fortified with Chlorine Dioxide (CD/MMS) and Dimethyl Sulfoxide (DMSO). Rebuilding the house after a tornado requires access to clean water, and the same goes for cellular regeneration and overall health.

My family and I have been using Berkey filters for nearly a decade. These gravity water filters remove hundreds of contaminants, including fluoride and heavy metals. Made of ceramic and housed inside a stainless-steel encasement, the Berkey filter system is a must when it comes to purified drinking water. After drinking this water for just a few weeks, it become readily apparent that its taste is much different than what you can buy at store.

Another recommendation for getting good, quality water is to Ozone your water with an Ozone generator. Ozoning[76] your water

---

75 I recommend this company as they produce a 3500mg bottle of CBD oil: http://bit.ly/MaryCBDOil

76 Ozone is a supercharged form of oxygen that contains an extra atom. Oxygen usually has two atoms; ozone has three. With extra oxygen molecules freely running around the body, it can attach itself to the bad and start reproducing the good. Ozoning can also be done through IV, autohemotherapy (blood is

purifies it from bacteria, viruses, spores, parasites, and chemicals, thus giving you more oxygen. Remember: oxygen is your friend and your body needs a *lot* of it! Oxygen is the lifeblood of your cellular system. Cancer, for example, deprives cells of oxygen, thus removing the one thing they desperately need to create energy and get rid of waste. "The prime cause of cancer is the replacement of normal oxygen respiration of body cells by an anaerobic cell respiration."[77] In other words, no oxygen, no cellular health. No cellular health, cancer and disease flourishes.

Dr. Tennant explains:

> When things are put into water to make the water some other drink, it changes how the water reacts in the body. If you take good water from a well or an uncontaminated stream, it will be alkaline (finding good water anywhere in the world is getting harder because of chemical contaminations). That means it contains electrons available for your body to use in its metabolism. However, if you put chlorine and/or fluoride in it, it becomes acidic. Anything that is acidic is an electron stealer. Anything that is alkaline is an electron donor.
>
> Your cells are composed of water, but it is also what your body uses to wash itself internally to clean away the garbage that gets in. Would you wash your car with coffee? Then consider washing the inside of your body with coffee or tea or sodas.

Avoid water in plastic bottles which are mass-produced by companies with bad water and even worse packaging! Your body needs clean water free of fluoride, free of contaminants, and infused with oxygen and alkalinity.

Miracle Mineral Solution (Chlorine Dioxide)

Chlorine dioxide is an FDA approved water purifier and is one of the best, safest, and most inexpensive detoxifying agents

---

taken out, ozoned, and put back in) or by ozone saunas. Hyperbaric ozone chambers are also widely used.

77 Bollinger, *Truth About Cancer*, 219.

known to man. Chlorine dioxide is *not* bleach, which is sodium hypochlorite. Typically referred to as the miracle mineral solution (MMS), CD is known to cure malaria within 24-28 hours! There are several benefits to CD, including boosting the immune system, healing wounds and rashes on the skin, detoxing pathogens and neurotoxins, treating autism, and a whole lot more.

CD is a 'selective killer,' which means it has the capability of destroying unwanted pathogens while leaving the 'good' in the body alone. It is noncarcinogenic; CD breaks down the bacterial cell wall, or when it comes to viruses, loosens the viral envelope, thus deactivating the cell while leaving human tissue alone. Functioning as an oxidizer, CD seeks and destroys rogue cells, killing pathogenic microorganisms, like viruses, fungi, and bacteria.[78] CD can be used to clean fruits and vegetables before consumption, thus ensuring that you're not ingesting something you shouldn't. I recommend picking up a copy of Jim Humble's book, *MMS Health Recovery Guidebook*, which can be ordered directly from his website.[79] In Humble's book, there are lots of various protocols for different health concerns, and this book is a regular staple in my house.

To maintain good overall health, you can take a dose of CD a few times each week. You only need to take 3 drops of CD mixed in a glass of filtered water a couple of times a week to keep up your good health. Remember the starting CD rule: "Low and slow is the way to go." When you are not in a viral emergency, begin with one drop of CD every hour for eight hours and work your way up to the 3-5 drop dose that your body can tolerate (i.e. no Herxheimer's Reaction). To accelerate this healing protocol, you can add DMSO on a 3-1 ratio to your CD. So, after you take your appropriate dose of CD in 4 ounces of water, take your glass and pour 4 more ounces of water in it, then add the correct amount of DMSO. (For example, if you took one drop of CD in 4 ounces of water, then put 3 drops of DMSO in the next 4-ounce glass of water. Drink one right after the other, no need to wait).

---

78   See Dr. Kerri Rivera's video/lecture at the HealthForAllOfLife.com website.
79   https://jimhumble.co/bookstore/mms-health-recovery-guidebook

Remember: *fear,* i.e., "emotional stress," is one of the three main forces that causes disease (the other two sources of stress being physical and chemical). If you're looking for more information on CD, please visit www.kerririvera.com and pick up a copy of her "Alternative First Aid Reference Guide."

DMSO

Nature's natural healer is made from wood pulp. DMSO binds with water, changing the structure of water at the cellular level. This process heals cellular damage and reduces 'free radicals' in the body. A lack of cellular health produces these free radicals which end up causing sickness, inflammation, and a host of other diseases. DMSO increases the permeability of the cell's membrane, thus allowing it to flush the toxins encamped within the cell. When the toxins are released and flushed out of the system, this naturally promotes the availability of oxygen to the cell, and thus it functions the way God intended it to function. DMSO is not toxic and does leave the body through the urine (there's no buildup).

"*Dimethyl sulfoxide* (DMSO) is an anti–inflammatory and analgesic compound that holds promise in managing a wide range of debilitating health conditions. DMSO is an approved pharmacological agent in more than 125 countries, and its safety and therapeutic effects are backed by nearly 50 years of research and more than 10,000 scientific articles on its biological implications."[80]

DMSO is used to treat all sorts of diseases and conditions: Alzheimer's disease; arthritis; atherosclerosis; Down's syndrome; drug extravasation injury (chemo damage); fibromyalgia; herpes; interstitial cystitis; malignancy; plastic surgery adjunct; prostatitis; reflex sympathetic dystrophy, scleroderma; spinal cord injury; stroke, and ulcerative colitis.[81] DMSO helps with allergies, immune function, joint pain, muscle pain, headaches, and sicknesses like bronchitis. This natural healer can be taken diluted or via a stick which can be rubbed on the feet, arms, or wherever you might need.

---

80 http://encognitive.com/files/DMSO%20cancer%20treatment.pdf
81 For more information, visit www.dmso.org.

As mentioned in the previous section on chlorine dioxide, DMSO can be taken with CD in order to enhance the healing process. *The DMSO Handbook for Doctors* (available on Amazon) contains a lot of different protocols for various health issues, so be sure to grab a copy.

> *ACTION STEP* – Consider using MMS/CD & DMSO every day and/or week!

TEN THINGS FROM CHAPTER FOUR

1) Jesus is the bread of life. He created nutrients and wants us to have them so we can serve Him and our neighbors.
2) The secret to a healthy life is developing healthy cells, and healthy cells can only be healthy to the degree that they receive the proper raw materials.
3) Stay away (!) from hydrogenated and partially hydrogenated oils, refined sugars, excitotoxins like MSG and Aspartame, and GMO's.
4) Studies have shown that fruits and vegetables fight cancer—and win. If these fruits and veggies can *fight* cancer, then they are foods that can *prevent* cancer, so get them in your diet. A lot!
5) In order to recover proper nutritional absorption and keep the cellular system running on all atomic cylinders, the most important thing to do is supplement your diet with the 'Mighty 90.'
6) 90 Essential Nutrients = 60 minerals, 16 vitamins, 12 amino acids, and three fatty acids.
7) Nitric, Humic, and Fulvic acid are essential! Moringa is the world's most powerful plant, and you should be using CBD oil regularly.
8) You need water because you *are* water!

9) Miracle Mineral Solution (MMS)/Chlorine Dioxide (CD) is significant in helping promote proper oxygenation at the cellular level.

10) Dimethyl sulfoxide (DMSO) is wood pulp derivative which has been shown to fight off various diseases.

Chapter Five

Detoxify

"He who covers his sins will not prosper, but whoever confesses and forsakes them will have mercy."

Proverbs 28:13

The Bible often decries the sins of man, citing them as a treasonous affront to the living God. Sin, which is the violation/transgression of the law of God (1 John 3:4), is a snub in that it stems from a rebellion, a 'kicking against the goads' (Acts 26:14), towards God and His loving desire for man. When man forsakes his image-bearing calling, he trades in his liberty under God's law word, and he is, in effect, in hot pursuit of his own self-induced, humanist slavery. He prefers his own way and everyone else, including God, can take a proverbial hike (Prov. 3:5-8). Here in Proverbs 28:13, we learn that those who cover their sins instead of confessing their sins will not prosper—they won't get ahead. Those who confess and forsake their sins, who develop a daily pattern of repentance—what we call 'mortifying,' or killing, their sin-stained flesh—will have *mercy*. We also know from 1 John 1:9 that "If we confess our sins, He is faithful and just to forgive us our sins and cleanse us from all unrighteousness."

If the correlation between Jesus Christ being the bread of life and our need to feast on Him and His word is akin to acquiring proper nutrition through healthy foods, supplementation, and healthy hydration, then there is another correlation between detoxing the body from harmful toxins and repentance of sin. In order to be spiritually healthy, the Christian must mortify his flesh; he must be on a quest to put sin on the cross and back in the tomb where it stays dead forever. The same goes for our physical lives as well. We must pursue health and part of pursing health is ridding ourselves of unhealthy patterns and foreign invaders. Toxins, heavy metals, chemicals—all of it creates havoc in the body and must be eradicated. That said, the key to building healthy cells is both healthy detoxification and developing a healthy immune and lymphatic system.

CELL BUILDING ESSENTIAL #3: HEALTHY DETOXIFICATION

Your body is intricately designed; it has a self-cleaning feature! If only our houses or cars had such a thing. The self-cleaning feature is your body's detoxification system, and your liver is the engine that drives the whole thing. Keep in mind what we said in chapter three. From the Wholistic perspective, your body is uniquely designed to heal itself with several systems in place to remedy the problem. Whenever there is a stressor, the body responds accordingly. Fevers, mucus, rashes, etc., are all the ways in which the body responds to foreign invasion. The fever, for example, is the symptom that tells you something has gone wrong. Allopathic medicine treats symptoms and never gets around to dealing with the *cause*. MDs, RNs, and the allopathic entourage will adopt a scorched-earth paradigm to do anything to suppress the fever, but they have no answer for how to get healthy or deal with what caused the fever in the first place. In this worldview, definitions are found wanting and so are the solutions.

The way to rebuild a home after the tornado strike is to clear the debris from the land. The debris in your body are the toxins, bacteria, and heavy metals that overburden the liver, which increases stress on the rest of the body. A sick, under-nutrified liver is a sick immune system, and a sick immune system is a cancer-ready environment. The key, as we outlined in the last chapter, is to keep the garbage out of your body through proper hydration and proper nutrition. These are the tools to help your detoxification system working efficiently. You can detox all you want, but if the body doesn't have the proper nutrients, the liver (for example) can't break down the toxins because it doesn't have the necessary nutrients. Which is why we nutrify *first*. Once this is in place, the sewage system of your body needs to be clear so as to remove toxins and promote overall health.

Your body is always in detox mode. Sweating, urinating, defecating, and breathing are all ways your body regularly detoxifies. But those systems can get 'clogged up' and create a bottleneck in the affected system. Smoking, for example, creates a tremendous bottleneck! Food can also contribute to the clogging. Preservatives, artificial flavorings and additives, artificial coloring, sweeteners, trans fats, and foods soaked in pesticides, herbicides, and fungicides all place tremendous stress on the body. Mercury fillings are also hugely problematic. If you take the trash out, that is, keep this stuff out of your body, you're well on your way to healing your gut, healing the liver, and healing the rest of the body.

The following suggestions are tools to help clear the debris.

Intermittent and Extended Fasting

Fasting is the least expensive protocol because you don't have to purchase a thing. It is also one of the most natural ways of promoting detoxification in the body. The key, however, is to drink a sufficient amount of filtered water while you refrain from eating. Fasting restricts calorie intake, which is linked to longevity. It also contributes to lower rates of all inflammation-related diseases. It is a natural beta blocker, a natural calcium channel blocker, and a natural blood thinner and statin drug. Fasting promotes the healing of the skin as well as blood vessels. It has also been shown to stimulate collagen production. In short: fasting is a natural way to 'reset' pretty much all of your biological systems.

Dr. David Jockers lists[82] the top 12 benefits of intermittent and extended fasting:

1. **Fat burning** – This helps you lose weight. Fasting helps your body to be more metabolically flexible and energy efficient, which in turn allows you to burn fat for energy rather than store it.

2. **Energy** – Everyone needs energy, and just about everyone wishes they had more if it. Fasting helps with mitochondrial biogenesis. If you are tired a lot and rely on energy drinks, coffee, and other processed stimulants to get you through the day, it's a sure sign that your mitochondria organelles are not performing well.

3. **Reducing inflammation** – Inflammation is linked to every single degenerative disease out there (heart disease, cancer, diabetes, Alzheimer's, Parkinson's, and autoimmune conditions). Fasting is a nutritional strategy to significantly reduce inflammation in the body.

4. **Stress Off the Digestive System** – Fasting heals the gut. The more foods that go in, which put stress on the digestive system, the more the gut lining breaks down. 'Leaky gut syndrome' is the result of toxicity and inflammation. Fasting puts the body into 'repair mode,' which weeds out the microbiome of the gut, which fosters healing and stem cell regeneration.

5. **Autophagy** – This is where the body breaks down the different parts of the cell that are damaged in order to create new, fully functioning parts. This process of cellular regeneration can be inhibited by nutritional deficiency and toxicity.

---

82 https://drjockers.com/fasting-lifestyle

6. **Genetic Repair** – During fasting, genes are stimulated in order to repair older cells, which is far more energy-conserving than producing new cells. Too much cellular reproduction can get out of hand quickly, which is what happens during the cancer process.

7. **Stem Cells** – These are baby cells which are resilient to stress. Fasting naturally stimulates stem cells, which are needed for repairing and regenerating the body.

8. **Insulin Sensitivity** – When you fast you improve your hormone sensitivity. Insulin is a fat-storage hormone, which also promotes inflammation. When your body produces insulin every time you eat, you're going to promote inflammation *and* store more fat. The better your sensitivity, the less insulin you need. The less insulin you need, the less inflammation you'll have. When all of this is corrected, the less fat you'll store.

9. **Reduce Chronic Disease** – Cellular health reduces diseases, period. Fasting is one tool in the toolbox to promote cellular health and reproduction.

10. **Relationship with Food** – Fasting helps you appreciate the food you are consuming. Instead of living to eat, you can eat to live. Rather than giving in to cravings and addictions to snacks and sugary drinks, fasting helps curb those unhealthy cravings.

11. **Enhanced Mental Health** – Healthy guts mean healthy brains. Healthy brains stave off depression. Fasting creates more ketones that reduce inflammation in the brain. Less inflammation means less brain fog, less addiction, and better mood and attitude.

12. **Spiritual growth** – Fasting helps us listen to the Holy Spirit. The reason Jesus fasted, and the reason He instructed his followers to fast, is because it helps us keep our focus on God. Biologically speaking, it clears your body. Spiritually speaking, it clears your soul.

Liver Detox

As I stated earlier, the liver is the engine which drives the detox train. When the liver has proper nutrition, its detoxify functions are astoundingly productive. This second largest organ is everything for your health!

Dr. Josh Axe recommends[83] the follow six things in order to detox the liver.

1. **Remove toxic foods from your diet**. Stop eating junk! No more processed foods, no more vaccines, no more artificial foods. No more! Eat real fruit, real vegetables, sprouted grains, and organic, grass-fed beef (if you prefer meat).

2. **Drink raw vegetable juice**. If eating vegetables is good, juicing them is better. Juicing vegetables has the benefit of easier digestion, which is what you want when trying to detox the liver. Your body will absorb the nutrients much better in this form. Something we juice rather often is carrots, kale, apples, oranges, turmeric, ginger, garlic, beets, parsley, and cabbage. An uptake in juiced veggies reduces acidity in the body, which helps cellular voltage and pH balance. One more added benefit is the high fiber content which assists the body's digestion process.

3. **Load up on potassium-rich foods**. It is recommended that we get 4,700 milligrams of potassium per day. Dr. Axe comments, "Potassium-rich foods help to lower systolic blood pressure, lower cholesterol, and support a healthy cardiovascular system, in addition to helping cleanse your liver." What foods should you eat? Sweet potatoes, tomato sauces, beet greens, spinach, beans, blackstrap molasses, and bananas.

4. **Coffee Enemas**. "Coffee enemas help with constipation, reduce fatigue, and aid in liver detoxification. An

---

83   https://draxe.com/nutrition/liver-cleanse

enema targets the lower portion of your large intestine and can be done at home… During the enema, organic coffee is retained in your bowel, allowing the fluid to enter the liver through the intestinal wall. This has a stimulating effect that increases bile flow, helping to jumpstart both your gallbladder and your liver. This sparks the production of the chemical glutathione, a strong cleaning compound that helps to release the buildup of toxins in your system." You can go to Dr. Axe's website to learn how to do one. [84]

5.   **Milk thistle, dandelion, and turmeric supplements.** Milk thistle is largely considered to be the king of all detoxifying herbs, which is helpful for a liver cleanse. Dandelion root is packed with vitamins and minerals, and has a natural diuretic effect, which translates to the liver eliminating toxins very quickly. Dandelion also helps strengthen the immune system. Turmeric is something my family and I consume quite a bit. Turmeric helps reduce joint pain by reducing inflammation. Dr. Axe notes that it is an effective antidepressant, aids in digestions, restores blood sugar balance, and supports healthy liver tissue and liver metabolism.

6.   **Eat beef liver or take liver tablets.** "Liver from young, healthy, grass-fed cattle or chicken liver is rich with vitamins A and B, folic acid, choline, iron, copper, zinc, chromium, and CoQ10. Liver is one of the most nutrient-dense foods we can eat." If you don't prefer to eat animal liver, liver pills are an option, however, Dr. Axe suggests, "Seek a supplement that guarantees no hormones, pesticides, or antibiotics are used in the feeding and care of the cattle."

---

84   I also highly recommend Dr. Jay Davidson's protocol: https://drjaydavidson.com/coffee-enema-missing-links/

Gallbladder Cleanse

Why do we have a bladder? Dr. Josh Axe explains,

> The gallbladder is a small organ in the shape of a "sac" that has the primary role of storing bile that's made in the liver. As part of the digestive system, the gallbladder helps communicate back and forth to other organs in order to perform functions, such as enzyme production and storage, chemical reactions that break down foods into nutrients, and elimination of waste.
>
> The gallbladder sits just under the liver, and the two organs have a close working relationship. The primary need for the gallbladder storing and recycling excess bile is so bile can be reused for the digestion of future meals. Bile helps enzymes in the body break down fats into fatty acids. Once bile is made in the liver, it travels to the gallbladder through a channel called the cystic duct. The gallbladder stores bile between meals so when we eat bile can be squeezed through the bile duct as needed and used to break down food before it makes its way to the intestines.
>
> If the gallbladder becomes inflamed, surgery to remove the organ is sometimes a last-resort option to prevent rupturing. Following removal, the gallbladder is not actually needed for survival or digestion because bile can be made to flow from the liver right into the small intestines. Therefore, the gallbladder is said to be a nonessential organ.[85]

Having a gallbladder problem can be painful. A dysfunctional, unhealthy gallbladder can result in pain in the abdomen and back; shooting pains in the stomach and mid-section of the body; nausea, loss of appetite, vomiting, trouble breathing, and fever. Cholecystitis,

---

85 https://draxe.com/health/gallbladder-symptoms

which is caused from gallstones, stems from inflammation and overload due to toxicity. Dr. Axe recommends: 1) Sticking to an anti-inflammatory gallbladder diet (plant foods and supplements; no processed food); 2) Exercise (20, 30 or 60 minutes per day); 3) Balance hormones naturally (diet and exercise); 4) Check medications (if you're on medication, speak with your doctor about getting off any hormone or cholesterol meds); 5) Consider supplements (same as liver detox protocols).

Kidney Cleanse

With all the talk about liver cleanses, the kidney cleanse is oftentimes ignored. Kidneys filter about 50 gallons of blood per day, and about one-half to two quarts of fluid and waste are taken out of the blood and passed through the body in our urine. There are three kidney cleanse herbs that Dr. Axe recommends: 1) Stinging nettle (high in vitamin; can get it in tea form); 2) Burdock root (another tea); and 3) Rehmannia (supplement form). Foods to implement: 1) High-antioxidant fruit (cranberries, black cherries, and blueberries); 2) Beets; 3) Seaweed (adding spirulina or chlorella to a juice or smoothie); 4) Lemon juice; 5) Spinach. Protocols can be found on Dr. Axe's website.[86]

Other Detoxing Essentials

1. **Wild Oregano.** Wild Oregano Oil is a powerful natural cleanser. Make sure it is "wild" *(not the kind you put on pizza)* and it has at least 75% carvacrol, which is the active anti-microbial agent in this spice. Because this spice is "hot," make sure to buy it with a carrier oil like extra virgin olive oil or grape seed oil. You can use this kind of oil topically or sublingually (under the tongue).
2. **Nascent Iodine.** Nascent Iodine is also a great detoxifier (and nutrient).[87]

---

86   https://draxe.com/health/kidney-cleanse
87   Learn more here: https://thetruthaboutcancer.com/detox-with-iodine

3. **Apple Cider Vinegar.** Vinegar has been used as a health remedy since the days of Hippocrates. The ancient Greek doctor treated wounds with it. "The extensive list of apple cider vinegar benefits has been well-known for centuries. It's been shown to keep blood sugar in check, amp up weight loss, and even improve the appearance of acne and scarring. Plus, apple cider vinegar consumption works great for the keto diet. Apple cider vinegar (ACV) is made from apple cider that has undergone fermentation to form health-promoting probiotics and enzymes, giving it significantly less sugar and fewer calories than apple cider or apple juice. In fact, it only takes one to two tablespoons of ACV to take advantage of the health benefits of apple cider vinegar and each tablespoon clocks in at just 3–5 calories and contains minimal sugar."[88]

4. **Bentonite clay.** You may have never heard of bentonite clay before. Individuals in various cultures refer to it as "healing clay" that cleanses the body. Bentonite clay is a product composed of ash taken from volcanoes. It is used for facial clay masks, ointments and pastes, and even hair treatments.[89]

5. **Colloidal Silver/Silver Hydrosol.** Silver is a trace mineral that is acquired through food and water, cow's milk and even breast milk. Of all the plants, mushrooms contain the highest amounts of silver. Silver is non-toxic and has many benefits to health. It acts as an antimicrobial substance, not an antibiotic, and retards fungal and bacterial growth. Silver boosts overall immune health by binding to viruses, taking the protein, and rendering it useless. When taken and working properly, silver can take back the DNA and RNA that the virus took from healthy cells. Silver can also be used to deal with candida.

---

88 https://draxe.com/nutrition/apple-cider-vinegar-uses
89 https://draxe.com/nutrition/10-bentonite-clay-benefits-uses

Advanced TRS (Toxic Removal System)

TRS is something my family and I have been using for quite a while and we've noticed tremendous benefits from using it. "Advanced TRS facilitates detoxification at the cellular level to attract, trap, and remove heavy metals, toxins, and other contaminants through the body's natural process. Zeolite (Clinoptilolite Zeolite), the active ingredient in Advanced TRS, facilitates your body's ability to extract harmful toxins. As zeolite is inert in your body, your body does not recognize it as anything out of the ordinary. However, heavy metals, radioactive elements and other toxins are extremely attracted to the cages-like structure of the zeolite molecules. In addition, zeolite will exchange its healthy negatively charged minerals for any positively charged toxins in your body. Because zeolite uses nanotechnology and is encapsulated in water clusters, it will go anywhere in your body water can."[90]

Known to detox aluminum, lead, mercury, cadmium, copper, arsenic, nickel, chromium, sulfur, and tin, TRS is a must-have if you want to rid your body of the major problem of heavy metal toxicity. There are many different Facebook groups which serve as great resources for learning about TRS and also hearing testimonials. You can purchase it from my website.[91]

ACTION STEP – Purchase the TRS from the link in the footnotes and start taking 3-4 sprays a day. You can work yourself up to 5 sprays a day, depending on your body's response. TRS is an amazing, natural way to rid the body of metals and from my own personal testimony, I can tell you that it *works*.

---

90   https://drjasongarwood.cosevatrs.com/the-science-of-trs/
91   https://drjasongarwood.cosevatrs.com

CELL BUILDING ESSENTIAL #4:
HEALTHY IMMUNE AND
LYMPHATIC SYSTEM

Detoxification involves far more than eating the right foods: it involves certain activities which stimulate the body's immune and lymphatic system. Recall the problem of the tornado destroying a house. How does one rebuild? One thing it definitely needs is a working sewer system. A strong immune and lymphatic system is the sewage system that keeps the pipes, as it were, from getting gummed up. Let's consider a few things as it pertains to these systems.

The Immune System

The immune[92] system, the body's natural operating system, is really *two* immune systems. They are the *cell-mediated,* and *humoral.* The cell-mediated system consists of many different kinds of immune cells and a multi-functional message system (think white blood cells). If we used military terms to describe it, we could say that it is the *air, land,* and *sea* attack controlled by different communication systems with the goal of seeking and destroying the "bad" stuff: viruses, bacteria, fungus, toxins, etc. When, for example, an unvaccinated child gets chicken pox, the cells are told to go to war, and that's what they do: it's their job. The end point is white blood cells which either 'eat' the infected cells or disarm the cells with biological mechanisms, but either way, they push them out of the body (which results in rashes or mucus).

Chicken pox and measles, for example, are fought off rather easily by this God-created system, as history has shown. When the frontline cellular armies do their job, they produce symptoms like

---

92   The word 'immune' comes from the Latin *immunis*, which means 'exempt from public service.' In other words, it means 'free from invasion, harm, or disease.' The immune system is like a border control agent assessing whether or not the invader is part of the body, or something altogether harmful. Once a pathogen is tagged as harmful, the body knows to deal with it as an enemy.

a fever, which isn't "sickness" but rather evidence that the body is ridding itself of something that shouldn't be there. In other words, God has created our bodies—down to every last cell—to *fight*. Our bodies were created good, fully capable of detoxing foreign invasions, and although we are broken because of sin, we need to recognize that we're in the process of restoration. We must not hinder that process through *disobedience* and *unhealthy patterns,* nor should we cavalierly attempt to artificially super-charge such systems with little to no regard for the litany of unintended consequences and side effects—which is what vaccines entail.

The humoral system is the part of the immune system that comes along *after* the fight is over, where the cell-mediated immune system hands over part of the antigen, so that a record of the infection-fight is backed up in the body's memory—lymph nodes, in the form of IgG antibodies. If the same antigen should come around in a few years, poking around to see if anyone is home, the body says, *"I remember you; you must now leave."* These antibodies attach to the remembered antigens and either kill the virus or toxin, or "mark them" so that other cells can come along and finish the job. God knew what He was doing...go figure.

Enter vaccines. Instead of trusting the immune system process, most vaccines, because they are killed microbes mixed with aluminum, primarily involve the humoral immune system. By design, vaccines trigger the rear-end action of the immune system—the humoral—and quiet down the front line, cell-mediated system. *The vaccine turns the core blueprints and functionality for the immune system upside down.*

Instead of allowing a child to get chicken pox and fight it the way his body is designed to fight, we inject him with the virus along with other toxins and culture-medium antigens in order to stimulate the humoral antibodies' response. In order to accomplish triggering the humoral system without the use of the front line, cell-mediated immune system, *adjuvants* have to be added to the vaccine: these ostensible "helpers" are irritants that force the humoral immune system to produce antibodies which are supposed to keep out the sickness in question. Vaccines are simply a back-door "trick play" on your immune system.

The basic scientific problem with vaccines, then, is the stimulation of antibodies in the humoral immune system, and the suppression of front-line cells in the cell-mediated system. There are two different, though similar, problems with vaccines. *One* is dysregulation of the immune system because the vaccine is now causing imbalance and mayhem in the system, which may result in a slew of reactions including allergies, autoimmune disorders, chronic illnesses, cognitive disorders, swelling of the brain, seizures, permanent brain injury, and death.

A *second* problem with vaccines is molecular mimicry where the immune system picks up from the antigen a small genetic sequence which is identical to normal human tissue. This can cause the antibodies to not only attack the antigens in the vaccine, but also begin to track cells in the body which look like the vaccine antigen. Like an angry drunk, the antibodies attack the nervous system, organs, and other vital tissues, wrecking the place without any intention on paying for damages. In other words, *never, ever* get a vaccine. If you've had vaccines, get the TRS I mentioned a few pages back and begin to detox your body from this garbage.

Regarding the 'boosting' of the immune system, it's really more of giving your immune system the proper tools to obtain homeostasis. The 7 CBE's give the immune system a fighting chance. Colds and flu, for example, are not something you catch, but something you "earn," as Dr. John Bergman likes to say. When the body experiences stress via toxic foods, air, low sunlight, stressful life circumstances, synthetic drugs and medications, less activity, vaccinations, nutrient deficiencies, and so on, your immune system is weakened. You didn't give it a fighting chance on account of your inactivity, stress, and having eaten Taco Bell for the fifth time this week. Pathogens are *already* in your body, so when the immune system is weak, things go sideways. When the pathogens gain a foothold in your body's poor terrain-environment, the body's responses follow naturally: increased mucus to wall off the invader, the release of histamines, fever, bronchus may inflame, cough and sneezing rise to eliminate mucus, diarrhea helps eject the pathogen, and so on.

So, without further ado, how do we strengthen the immune system? What should we avoid? Dr. Eric Berg suggests several things, starting first with what to *avoid*:

1. **Low nutrient foods**;
2. Don't adopt a **wrong diet** which avoids vitamins, trace minerals, amino acids, and fatty acids; (low-fat diets, for example, weaken your cells which contain two layers of fat walls)
3. Reduce **stress** in your life;
4. **Low sleep** damages the immune system;
5. Unhealthy **Glucose** levels

How to strengthen the immune system:

1. **Vitamin C** from food, or food concentrates (not synthetic); for example, sauerkraut, bell peppers, berries, green leafy vegetables, etc. Vitamin C stimulates the production of white blood cells; it is also stored in your adrenal glands which in turn produces adrenal hormones.
2. **Vitamin D** is an immune modulator and hormone factor, which means there are receptors in your white blood cells which controls the immune system. Vitamin D supports t-cells which is the boot camp for white blood cells. It protects against pathogens, aggressively killing unwanted microbes. This can be difficult to get from foods, so get plenty of sunshine!
3. **Vitamin A** provides the structural integrity of mucosal cells in the sinus and respiratory centers, which aid the immune system. Cod liver oil, butter, egg yolks, etc., are helpful because Vitamin A is a fat-soluble vitamin.
4. **Zinc** is the most important mineral for the immune system. It helps build t-cells and protects against viruses.

5.   **Garlic** is #1 in potency for killing off viruses, bacteria, yeast, fungus, and mold.
6.   **Colloidal Silver**, which is basically silver particles in water, starves off the oxygen supply to microbes. It can be used as a nasal rinse, and it is a potent anti-viral.
7.   **Olive leaf** is also an anti-viral that strengthens the immune system.

There is one more key component to building a healthy and effective immune system and that is **beta glucan**. Beta glucan, which is the best known naturally made autoimmune regulator, activates the immune system without overstimulating the immune system (which, as we have seen, is what vaccination does). Youngevity's RVB 300 or RYL 500 Beta Glucan are both excellent products.

Beta glucan activates both the innate and acquired immune system by binding to microphages (a type of white blood cell that detects intruders and coordinates a full-on assault against foreigners). When activated by beta glucan, microphages are put on high alert and devour invaders like Pac-Man does, a process known as phagocytosis. Microphages fortified by beta glucan are better equipped to fight off pathogens. When the microphages are running at full capacity, they enlist a communication system by telling the other defenders in the body to come and clean house. When the information transmitted by the microphages is used, these cells produce antibodies and t-cells, which are the Navy Seals of the body's natural immune system. Antibodies bind the foreigners, bring them to the microphages to be engulfed, and the invaders are neutralized.

Allergies

Allopathic, reductionist medicine reduces the issue of allergies down to one simple focus: the pollen (or the cat, for that matter). There are no 'cures' and only the symptoms can be tamed. Billions are spent each year to manage these 'seasonal' allergies. But think about this: if the problem is the dog or the cat, or the hay, or even the skin of the fruit, wouldn't *everyone* have an issue? Exactly.

The typical understanding of allergies goes like this: an allergen gets into the system, and the system doesn't like it for some genetic reason, so it responds with inflammation, mucus, and other unpleasantries. Some people are just allergic to some things, and that's the way it is. But the truth is, the allergen gets into someone and triggers a reaction *based on an already imbalanced body.* When your system is strong, no number of allergens will disturb you. When your system is stressed and out of whack, allergens cause problems.

Seasonal allergies, asthma, and other allergy attacks are typically caused by the foods and drinks we consume. Pollen and cats and whatever do play a role, but allergic reactions are exacerbated by improper nutrition. In other words, we're lacking in nutrients, and we're abundant in bad foods/drinks. MDs won't tell you that your digestive system is related to allergies, but the science backs this claim. In short, an immune system that is not experiencing homeostasis is stressed out, and the body is triggered by various environmental factors. The body needs 90 essential nutrients, and when it doesn't have them, adverse chemical reactions take place in the body because it's under attack or stressed, not primarily by dust and pollen, but by self-implosion.

The Lymphatic System

The lymphatic system, or sometimes called the lymphoid system, is connected to both the immune system and the circulatory system. Lymphatic vessels, nodes, and tissues carry the clear fluid called 'lymph' throughout the body and towards the heart. Similar to blood plasma, lymph returns proteins and fluid to the bloodstream. Tonsils, the thymus gland, and your spleen are all part of the lymphatic system. In short, the lymphatic system is the drain to the body's filters that keeps us clean and healthy. If the filters are clogged, we become toxic and sick. If you're overweight, you have a clogged lymphatic system and a weak immune system. When the lymphatic system is clogged, the vessels and nodes harden. To fix it, they need to be softened. In order to be softened, the body needs nutrition and movement. The main reason we need a healthy lymphatic system is to protect us from inflammation and illness.

Balancing fluids in the body is a key role with the system, as it protects from infections, bacteria, cancers, and such. Think of it as an inner-drainage system. Remember the sewer system? Here we are.

Dr. David Jockers explains the symptoms of lymphatic congestion:

- Fatigue
- Stiffness
- Muscle and joint pain
- Bloating
- Holding onto water
- Breast swelling during your cycle
- Itchy and dry skin
- Brain fog
- Headaches
- Weight gain
- Swollen glands
- Cold hands and feet
- Chronic sinusitis, colds, sore throats, or ear issues
- Skin problems
- Cellulite

How to fix it? Dr. Jockers gives us 8 ways[93] to clear the lymphatic system:

1. **Deep Breathing**: "Remember, your rib cage is a major lymphatic pump that is necessary for healthy lymphatic flow. This means that while exercise is essential for your lymphatic health, deep breathing is just as important. Deep diaphragmatic breathing allows your lungs to press into the thoracic duct which presses fluid back into your bloodstream. Deep breathing facilitates proper lymph movement and detoxification." He goes on to explain how to do it: "To practice deep diaphragmatic breath-

---

93 https://drjockers.com/lymphatic-cleansing/

ing, breathe deeply through your nose, hold it in for four counts, then exhale for two counts through your mouth. Gradually increase how long you hold and release your breath until you can hold 20 counts and exhale for 10 counts. Repeat this two to three times per session."

2. **Optimal Hydration**:"Lymph is about 95 percent water, hence it is not surprising that optimal hydration is absolutely key for the proper health and functioning of your lymphatic system. Without enough water, the lymphatic fluid cannot flow properly, which can lead to lymph congestion and dehydration. Water is absolutely essential to hydrate and rehydrate your body. Adding lemon or lime to your water can expedite the process of hydration and achieving a healthy lymph flow."

3. **Regular Exercise and Rebounding**:"Regular exercise can increase the oxygen supply to your tissues, stimulate blood circulation, help the transportation of oxygen to your tissues and cells and reduce toxic buildup. As a result, exercise not only facilitates a healthy immune response but may prevent cancer by reducing the risk of a low oxygenated environment in the body where cancer may grow." He goes on: "Rebounding is an increasingly popular low impact exercise that involves jumping on a trampoline. Rebounding promotes the flow of lymph through your body. It can increase the drainage of fluids and the removal of toxins."

4. **Dry Brushing and Healing Baths**: "Dry skin brushing or dry brushing is [a] technique that can boost circulation, lymphatic flow, and detoxification. This technique helps to remove dead skin cells and toxic waste, stimulate your sweat gland by opening your pores, improve immunity, prevent cellulite, initiate the development of new healthy skin cells, and promote lymphatic cleansing.... Healing baths are soothing baths that can boost your immunity, reduce stress, lower pain levels, and help relaxation. You can make healing baths by adding essential oils,

Epsom salt, sea salt, ginger, and other natural substances to your bath, all with different benefits. Essential oils, such as lavender or frankincense are fantastic for relaxation, an immune boost, stress relief, anxiety, and sleep. Epsom salt baths are fantastic for detoxification, circulation, and lymph flow. Sea salt baths are amazing for inflammation, detoxification, skin hydration, and skin issues."

5. **Specific Herbal Therapies**: Dr. Jockers recommends the following herbal therapies: Turkey Rhubarb, Sheep Sorrel, Slippery Elm Bark, Astragalus Root, Graviola Churchuasi, Bioactive Carbon, and formulated lymphatic system combination supplements.

6. **Alternating Showers**: "Taking alternate showers can stimulate your lymph system and provide an array of great health benefits. Cold showers and alternate showers may improve chronic pain, give you more energy, boost your brain function, and improve your mood."

7. **Massage Therapy**: "Having a massage is not only relaxing and pleasurable, but it has also been shown to improve your immune function and relieve symptoms of chronic pain and fatigue. Massage can increase the flow of the lymph fluid and blood flow to your muscles while reducing fluid buildup, preventing swelling, helping tissue repair, enhancing performance, and aiding in quick recovery….Lymphatic drainage massage is a specific form of specialized massage therapy designed to help your cells release toxic buildup, reduce lymph congestion, and help flush excess fluid within your tissues. It can lower your pain intensity as well."

8. **Sauna Therapy**: "There are over 80,000 toxic chemicals used regularly in the US and over 500 chemicals stored in the body of an average individual. Clearly, environmental toxicity is a huge concern that can lead to a clogged lymph system…. Perspiration through sweating is one of your body's key mechanisms to remove toxins. While exercising is essential for sweating and cleansing, infrared

sauna therapy is something you can also benefit from to improve your lymphatic function and which will benefit your overall health."

Essential Oils

Essential oils have increased in usage and for good reason: they are tremendous healing agents. Used throughout history, oils have various medicinal properties which can increase health and vitality. That said, what exactly are these oils and why are they essential? Dr. Josh Axe explains:[94]

Essential oils are extracted directly from the bark, flower, fruit, leaf, seed or root of a plant or tree, and just one drop can have powerful health benefits. They are typically created through the process of distillation, which separates the oil and water-based compounds of a plant by steaming.

Essential oils are highly concentrated oils that have a strong aroma. Sometimes they are called volatile aromatic oils because of their high concentration of the aromatic compounds. For example, the oil of "absolutes" is obtained from delicate flowers by either enfleurage or solvent extraction. Absolute oils often mimic the natural aroma of the plant and are also more colored and viscous than essential oils.

By concentrating the oils of these plants, you are literally separating the most powerful healing compounds of a plant into a single oil. For instance, *in order to get one single 15ml bottle of rose essential oil, it take 65 pounds of rose petals!*

---

94   https://draxe.com/essential-oils/essential-oils-guide/

Dr. Axe goes on to explain the top 15 essential oils and their health benefits:

1. **Clove**: Antibacterial, anti-parasitic and antioxidant protection.
2. **Cypress**: Improves circulation, reduces varicose veins, lifts confidence and can help heal broken bones.
3. **Eucalyptus**: Improves respiratory issues like bronchitis, sinusitis and allergies. Also invigorating and purifies the body.
4. **Frankincense**: Builds immunity, reduces inflammation, heals age spots, supports brain and may help fight cancer.
5. **Ginger**: Reduces inflammation, supports joints, improves digestion and relieves nausea.
6. **Grapefruit**: Supports metabolism and cellulite reduction. Mix with coconut oil and rub on areas of cellulite or take a few drops internally with water.
7. **Lavender**: Helps with relaxation, improves mood and heals burns and cuts.
8. **Lemon**: Great to use in homemade cleaning products as a natural antibacterial tool.
9. **Myrrh**: Natural antiseptic and may prevent or reduce infections and reduce inflammation of skin cells.
10. **Oregano**: Powerful antimicrobial properties, can kill fungus and help you kick a cold fast.
11. **Peppermint (or Mentha Piperita)**: Supports digestion, boosts energy, fever reducer, headache and muscle pain relief.
12. **Rose**: Incredible for reducing skin inflammation and great for creating glowing skin. Add a few drops to your facial moisturizer. Also, this is one of the most valued essential oils in the world at $1,000+ for 15ml.
13. **Rosemary**: Can naturally thicken hair, so it's great to add to homemade shampoos. Also, it improves brain function and memory so it's great to use when working, reading or studying.

14. **Tea Tree (Melaleuca)**: Natural anti-bacterial, anti-fungal, reduces bad odors and can help stimulate the immune system.

15. **Sandalwood**: Natural aphrodisiac that improves libido.

Essential oils are typically used in four ways: 1) Topically (with a carrier oil like coconut oil, almond oil, jojoba oil, etc.) 2) Aromatically (which gets the oils into the bloodstream); 3) Ingestion (they are powerful so should be used sparingly and diluted with water); 4) Personal Care (soaps, deodorants, toothpaste, bug spray, lotions, etc.).

I recommend Young Living, döTERRA, and/or Nature's Sunshine essential oils. Caution: don't buy the cheap stuff. Spring for the organic, non-synthetic, unadulterated, pure, therapeutic grade essential oils.

TEN THINGS FROM CHAPTER FIVE

1) Repentance from sin is akin to detoxing the body: we simply must get rid of the bad stuff.

2) Your body is always in detox mode. Sweating, peeing, defecating, and breathing are all ways your body regularly detoxifies.

3) Fasting is the least expensive protocol because you don't have to purchase a thing.

4) When the liver has proper nutrition, its detoxify functions are astoundingly productive. This second largest organ is everything for your health!

5) Liver, gallbladder, and kidney detoxes aid in overall health.

6) The immune system, the body's natural operating system, is really *two* immune systems. They are the *cell-mediated,* and *humoral.*

7) The body needs 90 essential nutrients, and when it doesn't have them, chemical reactions take place in the body because it's under attack, not primarily by dust and pollen, but by self-implosion.

8) The main reason we need a healthy lymphatic system is to protect us from inflammation and illness. Balancing fluids in the body is a key role with the system, as it protects from infections, bacteria, cancers, and such. Think of it as an inner-drainage system. Remember the sewer system?

9) 8 Ways to clear your Lymphatic system: Deep breathing, optimal hydration, regular exercise and rebounding, dry brushing and healing baths, specific herbal therapies, alternating showers, massage therapy, and sauna therapy.

10) Don't buy the cheap stuff. Spring for the organic, non-synthetic, unadulterated, pure, therapeutic grade essential oils.

CHAPTER SIX

Energize

"May the very God of peace sanctify you completely. And I pray to God that your whole spirit, soul, and body be preserved blameless unto the coming of our Lord Jesus Christ. Faithful is He who calls you, who also will do it."

1 Thessalonians 5:23-24

At the dawn of creation, the LORD God breathed life into Adam (Genesis 2:7). This Spirit-infused moment animated man to express the image of God in faithful service and obedience to God. The Hebrew word for 'spirit' and 'breath/wind', is the same word, and I don't think that's an accident. Adam was made from the dust, and the only reason he became an energized human was after God breathed into, or 'spirited' him. The animation of the breath of God is part of what it means to be human. We were nothing but soil, and then we were something. From dust to organized molecules, the Spirit of God brought us to energetic *life*.

It is true that God in Christ holds everything together (Hebrews 1:3a). This includes our neuropathways, the process of oxygen getting into the body through our noses, and the very cells that ward off foreign invaders. Christ holds our DNA *together*. What you must know, then, is that there is a reason for this: our sanctification. In the two verses listed at the start of this chapter, the apostle Paul explains that sanctification is something that will be eventually completed. This means that we must be blameless until the day we are fully and finally transformed into glory. We accomplish this not by merely sowing 'spiritual' things like prayer, but also sowing 'material/biological' things like eating right and making an honest effort at using the cell-building essentials. Note that Paul says, "whole spirit, soul, and body," the human trifecta. We are 'spirited' as God breathed life into us.

This threefold division—spirit, soul, and body—is equally important to God. Many Christians focus on the first two while ignoring that last part, the body. We want our bodies to be blameless before the Lord which means we must not only *stop* the habits of sluggishness that makes us lazy, uncommitted, and generally uninterested in expending energy, and start practicing a Christianity that is fueled by passion and the physical disbursement of energy which serves the healing of the nations. In other words, we are called to fulfill the dominion covenant, which dovetails with the great commission, and this requires a whole lot of effort. Just as the human body needs the Holy Spirit to have a regenerated heart in order to be saved, so the human body needs the energy of a fully functioning nervous system along with healthy blood, brains, bones, and skin in order to serve God and neighbor.

CELL BUILDING ESSENTIAL #5: HEALTHY NERVOUS SYSTEM

In order to return the damaged home to pristine condition, one must establish safe and reliable power lines in order to energize the home. The nervous system is the electrical system, the very core of what energizes the human body. One needs a sharp brain with proper voltage through routine aerobic exercise, wholistic dental care, quality sleep, and the application of electrons with electrical micro-currents and grounding. Only when necessary do you need natural pain relievers. So, how do we encourage this fifth cell-building essential?

Brain Health

The human brain is grand central station for what energizes the body. Neurotoxins and heavy metals through vaccines, bad food, and other toxic conditions are all things which can severely handicap the brain's functionality. When the brain's electrical currents are cut off, weakened, or deadened altogether, various health conditions exist: autism, dementia, Alzheimer's, ADHD, brain fog, poor memory, and even a lack of motivation. Your brain is thus nutritionally deficient and in need of help immediately.

Dr. Josh Axe explains[95] the top 10 brain-building breakthroughs:

1. **Yoga.** To be sure, the pagan/Buddhist accoutrements to this practice of 'emptying the mind' should be jettisoned, but stretching and breathing exercises while consciously thinking about your body movements and workings can be a therapeutic way to connect the brain to muscle activity. Yoga can be, without any religious apostasy, a helpful tool in improving flexibility and proprioception. Proprioception is simply the mind's awareness of the body's movement. This activity stimulates the brain's pathways to the rest of the body, which, when under concentration and deep breathing, floods the body with oxygen, the very thing it needs most.

2. **Juggling.** Juggling assists the brain's connections with the rest of the body through hand to eye coordination. When our eyes are functioning in tandem with the brain, memory loss and fatigue has been scientifically shown to be reduced.

3. **Meditation.** Through the mental contemplation of certain biblical truths, meditation grounds the emotional,

95   https://youtu.be/vh5NTA1L-wI

spiritual, and physical aspects of your body, keeping focus on the things that matter. Practicing meditation on God's Word is nourishment for every aspect of your person and provides a foundation for your emotional and neurological health. "Bless the Lord, oh my soul!"

4. **Rosemary**. One of the most powerful plants in providing the brain with fuel, rosemary and rosemary essential oil should be a regular part of your diet. Rosmarinic acid is anti-inflammatory (which is crucial for brain optimization) and improves focus and memory function. Tip: use rosemary essential oil on your temples, neck, forehead, and under the nose for optimal brain stimulation.

5. **Omega-3 Fatty Acids**. Many people are lacking in omega 3's. Having this fatty acid is crucial for cellular health. Fatty fishes (salmon, tuna, and other wild-caught fish) provide omega 3 fatty acid. If you aren't eating fish, get it in a supplement. (See #7!)

6. **Learn Something New**. If you spend your time reading, learning a new activity, or actively challenging yourself in the realm of education and problem solving, you activate the brain's chemistry which improves overall health.

7. **Walnuts**. This nut actually looks like a brain! Walnuts are packed with omega-3 fatty acids, magnesium, antioxidants, and other vitamins and minerals.

8. **Runners High**. Increased circulation through exercise distributes oxygen and nutrients to the body, which improves focus and memory.

9. **Intermittent Fasting**. Helps clear the brain from unwanted conditions like inflammation. When you eat, there is a strong connection between the brain and the gut. Bad food, for example, gets to the brain through a leaky gut and thus hurts the brain. Fasting gives the body a break so your gut lining (and small intestine lining) can be repaired and thus the body can digest properly. Proper digestion helps the brain immensely.

10. **Certain Mushrooms**. Lion's Mane mushrooms, for example, help the brain. There are other foods to consider as well, things like avocados, beets, and turmeric.[96]

Sympathetic and Parasympathetic Nervous Systems

The body has what's called an Autonomic Nervous System (ANS). 'Autonomic' refers to the involuntary, automatic system that works on autopilot. You don't have to tell your body to digest food or breathe, it just happens. This is the ANS. The system turns the body up or down, or even on and off, depending on certain conditions related to homeostasis. If things are bad and the body is in 'freak out' mode, certain measures take place without you even realizing it! Within the ANS there are two functions: Sympathetic ('Fight or Flight') and Parasympathetic ('Rest, Sleep, and Digest').

The sympathetic mechanism pertains to the body's ability to react to stress. When danger approaches you, what happens? Do you run, or do you fight? Adrenaline kicks in, and hormones are enlisted to deal with the physiological stress. This is the 'on' switch. In contrast, the parasympathetic mechanism is the 'off' switch, which helps you relax. Rest, sleep, and digestion are all functions of the parasympathetic system. When you're in constant stress, you can't rest, and you can't digest. Metabolism works within this system. Processing nutrients is done when the body has proper rest.

In order to be healthy, you simply must have a healthy balance between the sympathetic and parasympathetic systems. When you're in a constant state of stress, you can see the effects: lack of focus, lack of sleep, unable to 'turn off' the brain, irritation, anger, etc. When your body is stuck in stress, you become 'burnt out,' which results in sluggishness, brain fog, and abnormal fatigue. Recovery from stress is the job of the parasympathetic system, which means that it is the key to balancing your hormones and other physiological issues. For example, when you exercise, the sympathetic turns on to provide the energy necessary to accomplish the task. When you're done, the

---

96 https://draxe.com/nutrition/15-brain-foods-to-boost-focus-and-memory/

parasympathetic helps you recover. This 'ebb and flow' is normal, until it's not!

All sickness is related to the ANS. If you want to heal, you have to calm the body down, plain and simple. To calm the body down, you have to have a functioning parasympathetic system. To activate the parasympathetic system, Pharmacist Ben Fuchs recommends: supplementation with the Mighty 90 essential nutrients (especially niacin!); slow, deep breathing exercises every day (exhaling activates the parasympathetic system); yawning (which is good!); softening and relaxing facial muscles (and tongue) through self-massage; relaxing muscles through intentional rest; rubbing/massaging hands (palms); meditation; paying attention to feet; stretching then relaxing; hot water; listening to relaxing sounds and music; and proper sleep.

> _**ACTION STEP**_ – Practice the Sabbath God has graciously given to us! Be sure you're resting and 'unplugging' from regular rhythms of work. Get plenty of sleep at night and by all means, have a proper balance between work and rest.

Exercise

We've already touched on this a bit, but it is worth repeating. Rebounding, walking, bike riding, hiking—all of these 'movements' of the body help strengthen the nervous system, which gives you the energy you need to carry out the dominion mandate. Your muscles, according to Dr. Tennant, are "battery packs" that need daily recharging in order to give the voltage your body needs to make healthy cells. Dr. Al Sears's P.A.C.E. program can help you recharge in only 12 minutes a day: _**Progressively Accelerating Cardiopulmonary Exertion.**_[97]

In order to help the heart reach its muscular capacity, we need higher intensity in shorter bursts. In other words, an increase in

---

97   https://youtu.be/6eT57VReSc0

intensity is actually better than an increase in time. Working one muscle group at a time, in a particular sequence, challenges the heart and lungs without fatiguing any one individual muscle. Doing this challenges the metabolic rate, which in turn burns fat.

- **Weight Loss vs. Fat Loss** – Focusing on weight loss is actually a mistake. Losing weight could mean losing bone density, fat, muscle, internal organ weight, or water weight. Rather than losing weight, we should be more specific: lose *fat*. Muscles burn calories; losing muscles means losing the engine that burns fat. Weight loss is the wrong approach.

- **Reprogramming Your Body** – Durational/exertional activity does not equal health. Short bursts of varying exercises have shown to burn more calories (upwards of nine times more body fat!). The key is knowing that we don't just burn calories while exercising, we burn them while resting as well. Short burst exercising tells the body to store energy for the next 'quick burn', and thus you have a more equal scale of burning and storing. When energy is stored in the muscle, you can 'feel' it, because you feel more energized! The storehouse of energy in the muscle keeps the body balanced and fat can be burned over the long haul.

When we age, we store calories in the form of fat, and thus we feel lethargic and tired. Exercising in short bursts reprograms the body to not rely on fat for fuel, but on the muscular storehouses instead. You are weaning the body off of fat and insisting on muscular calories for energy. Over time, the fat is unnecessary and is discarded.

From Dr. Sears' free eBook:

Burning fat during exercise tells your body it needed the fat. This trains your body to make more fat for the next time you exercise. Your body replenishes your fat each time you eat and becomes efficient at building and preserving fat necessary for long aerobic sessions in preparation for the next endurance workout. In doing so, it sacrifices muscle and preserves fat.[98]

ACTION STEP – Exercising through the following simple, cost efficient means: Jump roping, jumping jacks, burpees; running in place; squatting, step-ups, resistance band training, push-ups, planking, lunges, bicycle crunches, hiking, bike-riding, swimming, and just about anything that gets you moving!

Sleep

The Macmillan dictionary defines sleep as "a naturally recurring state of mind characterized by altered consciousness, relatively inhibited sensory activity, inhibition of nearly all voluntary muscles, and reduced interactions with surroundings." In other words, that thing you have to do each night! The problem for many, however, is that the quality of sleep has deteriorated as we find ourselves more and more dependent on energy drinks, coffee, and other quick 'fixes.'

People today are sleep deprived, which isn't good as it spurs on chronic health problems. Sleep deprivation in the short-term causes the release of stress hormones, elevates LDL cholesterol, elevates blood sugar, and reduces blood supply to the gut. In the long term, sleep deprivation debilitates us physically, mentally, emotionally, and spiritually. It weakens our immune system and contributes to higher disease rates. As we've seen already, this can muddle up your sympathetic and parasympathetic systems. Consider how a lack of sleep increases the risk of the following problems: cardiovascular disease, diabetes, cancer, obesity, memory loss, Alzheimer's disease, Parkinson's, multiple sclerosis, gastrointestinal disorders, kidney disease, dementia, stomach ulcers, constipation, depression, and other mental disorders.

---

98 https://marketing.alsearsmd.com/acton/media/28028/pace-the-12-minute-fitness-revolution

The importance of the autonomic nervous system must be underscored again: diaphragmatic breathing is controlled by the ANS. If you're not sleeping and experiencing a stress-filled lifestyle, the ANS won't do its job and you'll snore, or worse, you'll experience sleep apnea. The answer isn't a mask to wear at night, either. Chiropractic care stimulates the nerves that supply the lungs; losing weight improves quality of sleep; staying away from alcohol, tobacco, and other sedatives will keep your throat muscles relaxed; sleeping on your side, elevating the head, and maintaining regular hours for sleeping (stop staying up so late!) can not only fight against sleep apnea, it will increase the functionality of the ANS as well.

ACTION STEP – Go to bed! Stop staying up late eating ice cream and chips. Reduce blue-light exposure before bedtime (in other words, don't be on your phone!)[99] Increased blue light decreases melatonin production and you *need* melatonin to regulate the circadian clock and help you experience restful sleep. Get plenty of sunlight, use dim red lights for night lighting, use blue light blocking glasses if need be. Dr. Bergman recommends *no* stimulating or stressful activities before bedtime, no stimulants like caffeine, no dark chocolate, no alcohol (it disrupts REM: rapid eye movement), avoid spicy foods before bed, avoid grains and sugars, no work 2-3 hours before bed, and reduce or eliminate all medication. Dr. Bergman recommends that we do: stimulate the parasympathetic nervous system (chiropractic care), keep a regular sleep schedule and routine, regular meditation, aromatherapy, and deep breathing, regular exercise, eliminate EMFs (electro-magnetic fields which are electric currents that can and will mess with the voltage of cells[100]), and sleep with a room temperature no higher than 70 degrees Fahrenheit (if possible).

---

99 https://ntp.niehs.nih.gov/whatwestudy/topics/cellphones/index.html
100 http://www.5gappeal.eu/the-5g-appeal/

Wholistic Dental Care

Believe it or not, your teeth are connected to your nervous system! The body has 26 nerves in the mouth, and each are connected to the brain, spinal cord, and the rest of the nervous system. A problem with a tooth can wreak havoc on an organ and vice versa. One of the worst things you can do is have a root canal. Because the teeth are connected to the meridian (or electrical circuit) of the body, a dental problem can contribute to various diseases and illness. Did you know that 97% of terminal cancer patients have had root canals?[101] "Root-canaled teeth are essentially "dead" teeth that can become silent incubators for highly toxic anaerobic bacteria that can, under certain conditions, make their way into your bloodstream to cause a number of serious medical conditions—many not appearing until decades later."[102]

Wholistic dental treatment considers the electrical impact of dental care while trying to keep toxins out of your body. As you may expect, this includes the removal of mercury fillings which deteriorate the structural integrity of the tooth and leak into the body via the blood stream. One final thing: stay away from fluoride at all cost! The Advanced TRS recommended in a previous chapter helps remove fluoride from the body, but it does no good if you're using toothpaste that contains fluoride. Try a more organic type of toothpaste, or even some homemade ones you can find on various natural-minded websites.

> *ACTION STEP* – If you've had a root canal, get the tooth pulled as soon as possible. You may not notice anything, but it is a silent killer as it does cause a host of problems. Remove mercury fillings as soon as possible. Oil pulling (coconut oil) is a helpful practice as well. Simply take a spoonful of organic coconut oil, swish it around your mouth for 15-20 minutes,

---

101 https://realfarmacy.com/97-of-terminal-cancer-patients-previously-had-this-dental-procedure/
102 Ibid.

and spit it out. The oil 'pulls' bacteria out of your teeth and mouth, and thus promotes healing. You can also make it a regular practice to swish MMS/Chlorine dioxide in your mouth to help provide oxygen to the mouth and teeth.

Voltage and Grounding/Earthing

As outlined in a previous chapter, the body needs proper voltage in order to be healthy. In order to make new cells, the cells each need -50 millivolts of energy. Chronic diseases and cancer are all connected to a lack of proper voltage. To get well, you need to fix your voltage. There are three things that Dr. Tennant recommends: 1) Using the Tennant Biomodulator, which measures voltage and puts electrons into the body (essential oils, homeopathics, or Tesla lights help as well); 2) Proper nutrition (especially iodine, iron, zinc, selenium, glutathione, cortisol, and progesterone); 3) Detoxing & the removal of microbial enemies (MMS or homeopathics).

Another aspect to proper voltage is 'earthing', or what is sometimes called 'grounding.' In the medical context, to be 'grounded' or 'earthed' means that "our bodies are connected to the surface of the earth and its abundant supply of electrons. This is a natural condition in which earth's electrons spread over and into our bodies, stabilizing our internal electrical environment" (Dr. James Oschman).

Perhaps the most natural, inexpensive, and powerful therapy there is, grounding has been shown to: rapidly reduce inflammation, rapidly reduce chronic pain, rapidly improve blood flow, increase energy, improve sleep, and accelerate healing from injuries or surgery. Exposure to sunlight produces vitamin D in the body, and that's absolutely essential for health. When we're exposed to the 'ground,' we are thus granted a sort of electrical nutrition—in the form of electrons. The body needs electrons to get healthy so that cells have proper voltage, and so cells can make new ones. You don't 'fix' unhealthy cells; you have to make new ones.

Because earthing is so closely associated with paganism (this is because Christians have left a vacuum by refusing to do the science and participate in naturopathic modes of healing), we need to stay focused, theologically speaking. God is the Creator we are the created. We are made from the dust of the earth, as we talked about at the start of this chapter. As such, the earth is a gift to be utilized and stewarded, not disregarded and ignored. Grounding *does* in fact heal the body, and the common creational paradigm we share with the material world is meant to be advantageous to us.[103]

> *ACTION STEP* – Watch the *Down to Earth* documentary on YouTube. Go outside and walk in the grass without shoes, and certainly without socks! Go to the beach and keep your bare feet to the sand and in the water. Wear sandals and practice grounding whenever and wherever you can! I also recommend picking up two books: *Earthing*[104] and *The Earth Prescription*.[105]

CELL BUILDING ESSENTIAL #6: HEALTHY BLOOD, BRAIN, BONE, & SKIN

The sixth cell-building essential is akin to the installation of a new HVAC system after the tornado strike. Having healthy blood, bone, and skin is one more 'essential' aspect to healthy living. Your blood, for example, must be clean and oxygen rich in order to have a strong circulatory system. Pharmacist Ben Fuchs explains,

> Behind 'disease sick cells,' dirty blood is always to be found. It is the blood that is responsible for keeping the cells healthy. Blood is the five liters of sanguine fluid that winds through the nearly 50,000 miles of circulatory vessels, delivers food in the form of vitamins and minerals, drops off energizing oxygen, and drains away the acids and poisons produced by the

---

103 See: https://bioinitiative.org
104 https://www.earthing.com
105 By Dr. Laura Koniver. See her website: https://www.intuition-physician. com

cell as a part of its normal metabolism. If all disease is cell disease, all cell disease is the disease of dirty blood. The Bible says that the life of the flesh is in the blood and there's some very good reasons for that. It's the blood that delivers oxygen and nutrients to cells and cleans out their environment. Blood also generates an electrical charge as it moves around the body. Without effective circulation, the movement of electricity weakens, toxicity accumulates, and cells gradually start to suffocate, leading to hypertension, heart disease, chronic nose bleeding, arterial blockages, and blood cancers.

In fact, all illness and ultimately aging and death can be thought of as a function of sticky blood. In order to keep the blood circulating effectively, regular exercise is important. Moving the muscles help support the heart's pumping action. You want to avoid problem foods that reduce intake of processed and refined carbs, as digestive toxicity and elevated blood sugar are major sources of blood viscosity.

Vitamin E and omega-3 fatty acids from fish, flax and chia seeds have blood lubricating benefits and nothing beats oxygen for fluidity in the blood. So practicing slow deep breathing techniques is a must for eliminating illness and promoting longevity.

When it comes to high blood pressure (hypertension), cho-lesterol, anemia, and diabetes, there's a lot to consider and it can be overwhelming. However, it doesn't have to be. The aforementioned blood conditions are an enigma to the allopathic world, but there's a much simpler explanation for dealing with these conditions. Before we get into that, we need to know what the purpose of blood truly is.

Blood supplies oxygen to tissues while also supplying nutri-ents such as glucose, amino acids, and fatty acids; it removes the waste of carbon dioxide, urea, and lactic acid; your blood provides crucial immunological functions, white blood cells, and detects foreign material by antibodies; it has the feature of coagulation, which is one part of the body's self-repair mechanism; blood contains messenger functions, transports hormones, and signals tissue damage; the blood regulates your body's pH, and regulates the core body temperature.

Hypertension and Cholesterol

That said, what about high blood pressure and cholesterol? To begin, cholesterol doesn't clog arteries, and it's vital for hormone production. The allopathic message about lowering cholesterol is a smokescreen for more pharmaceutical drug consumption. Did you know that *far* more people die of heart disease with *low* cholesterol than those who die of heart disease with *high* cholesterol?[106] The problem isn't high cholesterol—it's high for a reason. A poor diet with lots of inflammation in the body is the real enemy. Focusing on lowering cholesterol is the wrong presupposition.

The way to deal with these complications is figuring out ways to lower your inflammation levels. Think of it this way: when the body has inflammation issues, the veins are stressed, and cholesterol is summoned to come along and help. The LDL cholesterol (low-density lipoprotein) comes along to patch up the holes and damage in the veins due to inflammation. When you continue eating garbage, the body, being the intelligently designed thing that it is, keeps summoning the cholesterol to fix the problems caused by the junk you're eating. When the cholesterol keeps coming, the pathways (veins) for the blood gets shrunken, and your blood pressure goes up. Yes, you're going to end up with hypertension and heart disease, but the problem isn't the cholesterol, it's the fact that you keep eating fast food (among other things). This is why popping more statin drugs won't actually help you.

---

106 Some studies claim that 75% of people who die of heart disease had low cholesterol!

Diabetes

Diabetes is an illness which stems from elevated blood sugar. When eating, the body deploys insulin to deal with carbohydrates, sugar, and fats. When you can't release the insulin anymore, you have diabetes. Insulin is a hormone released by the pancreas that is broken down and transported at the cellular level in order for the cells to use it as energy. Type 1 diabetes is an autoimmune disease where the immune system attacks the insulin-producing beta cells in the pancreas and typically affects people under the age of 20. Type 2 diabetes is more common, and this typically affects people over the age of 40. In this scenario, insulin is being released, but the body's response to it isn't appropriate.

At any rate, the real question is, how do we fix it? To start, we need to know the contributing factors. Dr. Axe lays out[107] a few things that contribute to diabetes:

- Having a poor diet
- Being overweight
- Having high levels of inflammation
- Living a sedentary lifestyle
- Experiencing high amounts of stress
- Having a family history of diabetes (especially a parent or sibling)
- Having high blood pressure or a history of heart disease
- Having a hormonal condition (like hyperthyroidism, poly-cystic ovary syndrome or Cushing's syndrome)
- Being exposed to toxins, viruses, or harmful chemicals
- Taking certain medications (like those that disrupt insulin production)

---

107 https://draxe.com/health/how-to-reverse-diabetes-naturally-in-30-days-or-less/

So how can someone reverse diabetes? Dr. Axe[108] gives us 5 steps:

1.   Remove These Foods to Reverse Diabetes Naturally

    a.   *Refined Sugar:* Refined sugar rapidly spikes blood glucose, and soda, fruit juice and other sugary beverages are the worst culprits. These forms of sugar enter the bloodstream rapidly and can cause extreme elevations in blood glucose. Even though natural sweeteners like raw honey and maple syrup are better options, they can still affect blood sugar levels, so only use these foods on occasion. Your best option is to switch to stevia, a natural sweetener that won't have as much of an impact.

    b.   *Grains:* Grains, especially gluten-containing grains like wheat, contain large amounts of carbohydrates that are broken down into sugar within only a few minutes of consumption. Gluten can cause intestinal inflammation, which affects hormones like cortisol and leptin, and can lead to spikes in blood sugar. I recommend removing all grains from your diet for 90 days as your body adjusts to this healing program. Then you can try bringing sprouted ancient grains back into your diet in small amounts.

    c.   *Conventional Cow's Milk:* Conventional cow's milk and dairy products should be eliminated, especially for people with type 1 diabetes. Dairy can be a fantastic food for balancing blood sugar if it comes from goats, sheep or A2 cows. But stay away from all other forms of dairy because the A1 casein produced by conventional cows will harm the body and trigger an immune response similar to gluten.

---

108 Ibid.

When buying dairy, only purchase raw and organic products from pasture-raised animals.

d. *Alcohol*: Alcohol can dangerously increase blood sugar and lead to liver toxicity. Research published in *Annals of Internal Medicine* found that there was a 43 percent increased incidence of diabetes associated with heavy consumption of alcohol, which is defined as three or more drinks per day. Beer and sweet liquors are especially high in carbohydrates and should be avoided.

e. *GMO Foods*: GMO corn, soy and canola have been linked to kidney and liver disease and may promote diabetes. I suggest removing all GMO foods and all packaged foods from your diet. Opt for products that are labeled organic or GMO-free.

f. *Hydrogenated Oils*: Remove hydrogenated, rancid oils from your diet, including vegetable oil, soybean oil, cottonseed oil and canola oil. Because these oils are processed, treated at very high temperatures, and combined with bleaching agents and artificial dyes, consuming them has been linked to many health concerns, including diabetes.

2. Incorporate These Foods to Treat Diabetes

a. *Foods High in Fiber*: Research shows that 90 percent of the U.S. population doesn't consume enough fiber on a daily basis. High-fiber foods help slow down glucose absorption, regulate your blood sugar levels and support detoxification. Aim to eat at least 30 grams of fiber per day, which can come from vegetables (like Brussels sprouts, peas and artichokes), avocados, berries, nuts and seeds, especially chia seeds and flaxseeds.

b. *Foods High in Chromium*: Chromium is a nutrient that's involved in normal carbohydrate and lipid metabolism. Foods high in chromium can improve the glucose tolerance factor in your body and naturally balance out blood glucose levels. It plays a role in insulin pathways, helping bring glucose into our cells so it can be used for bodily energy. Broccoli has the highest amounts of chromium, but you can also find it in raw cheese, green beans, brewer's yeast and grass-fed beef.

c. Magnesium-Rich Foods: Magnesium can help regulate blood sugar levels because it plays a role in glucose metabolism. Research shows that diabetes is frequently associated with magnesium deficiency. Eating magnesium-rich foods (like spinach, chard, pumpkin seeds, almonds, yogurt and black beans) can improve type 2 diabetes symptoms.

d. *Healthy Fats*: Medium-chained fatty acids found in coconut and red palm oil can help balance blood sugar levels, and they serve as the preferred fuel source for your body rather than sugar. Using coconut milk, ghee, and grass-fed butter can also help balance out your blood sugar levels, so include these foods into your meals and smoothies. Some research actually suggests that a high-fat, low carb diet known as the keto diet may be a novel approach to reverse diabetes naturally, although you don't technically have to go into ketosis to achieve the benefits of healthy fats in treating diabetes.

e. *Clean Protein*: Eating protein foods has a minimal effect on your blood glucose levels, and it can slow down the absorption of sugar. Some of the best sources of clean protein include wild-caught fish, which contains omega-3 fats that reduce inflammation, grass-fed beef, organic chicken, lentils, eggs, and bone broth.

f. *Foods with a Low Glycemic Load*: The glycemic index of a food tells you about the blood glucose-raising potential of the food. Foods that have a high glycemic index are converted into sugar after being eaten more quickly than low glycemic foods. If you are fighting diabetes, stick to low glycemic foods like non-starchy vegetables, stone fruits and berries, nuts, seeds, avocados, coconut, organic meat, eggs, wild-caught fish, and raw pastured dairy.

3.   Take These Supplements for Diabetes

    a.   *Chromium Picolinate:*Taking 200 micrograms of chromium picolinate three times daily with meals can help improve insulin sensitivity. A review published in *Diabetes Technology and Therapeutics* evaluated 13 studies that reported significant improvement in glycemic control and substantial reductions in hyperglycemia and hyperinsulinemia after patients used chromium picolinate supplementation. Other positive outcomes from supplementing with chromium picolinate included reduced cholesterol and triglyceride levels and reduced requirements for hypoglycemic medication.

    b.   *Cinnamon.* Cinnamon has the ability to lower blood sugar levels and improve your sensitivity to insulin. A study conducted at Western University of Health Sciences in Pomona, California found that the consumption of cinnamon is associated with a statistically significant decrease in plasma glucose levels, LDL cholesterol, and triglyceride levels. Cinnamon consumption also helped increase HDL cholesterol levels. To take advantage of the many health benefits of cinnamon, add one teaspoon to food, smoothies or tea. You can also take one to two drops of cinnamon essential oil internally by adding it to food or tea, or combine three drops of cinnamon oil with half a teaspoon of coconut oil and massage it into your wrists and abdomen.

c. *Fish Oil*: Taking a fish oil supplement can help improve markers for diabetes by reducing triglyceride levels and raising HDL cholesterol levels. Research published in the *Journal of Research in Medical Sciences* shows that omega-3 fatty acids found in fish oil are necessary for proper insulin function, preventing insulin intolerance and reducing inflammation. To use fish oil as a natural remedy for diabetes, take 1,000 milligrams daily.

d. *Alpha Lipoic Acid*: Alpha lipoic acid is an antioxidant that helps turn glucose into fuel for the body. It effectively improves insulin sensitivity and reduces symptoms of diabetic neuropathy, such as weakness, pain and numbness that's caused by nerve damage. Although our bodies make alpha lipoic acid and it can be found in some food sources, like broccoli, spinach, and tomatoes, taking an ALA supplement will increase the amount that circulates in your body, which can be extremely beneficial when trying to reverse diabetes naturally.

e. *Bitter Melon Extract*: Bitter melon helps lower blood glucose levels, and it regulates the body's use of insulin. Studies show that bitter melon extract can help reduce and manage symptoms of diabetes, including insulin resistance, heart complications, kidney damage, blood vessel damage, eye disorders, and hormone irregularities.

4. Following an Eating Plan

a. Dr. Axe lays out those meals on his blog, which is footnoted below. (This author strongly recommends a whole food, plant-based diet).

5. Exercise to Balance Blood Sugar

    a. Exercise reduces chronic disease and can help reverse diabetes naturally. Studies show that exercise improves blood glucose control and can prevent or delay type 2 diabetes, while also positively affecting your blood pressure, heart health, cholesterol levels, and quality of life.

ACTION STEP – Stop eating packaged and processed food which has bad fats, sugars, and unhealthy oils. Consume the Mighty 90, especially the essential fatty acids, like Omega 3s. Lighten the load of grains and gluten—they will inflame the body.

Bones & Joints

Arthritis drugs are a major seller on the pharmaceutical market. It is assumed that when someone gets old, he or she will need to get on an arthritis drug because arthritis and osteoporosis are simply natural facts of life. Right? Wrong. First, no one gets arthritis because they're lacking in pharmaceutical drugs. Second, bones and joints are always in a state of regeneracy; they are constantly seeking to replace themselves.

Two things are happening in your body as it pertains to bones: 1) Osteoclasts are constantly breaking down bone tissue to get rid of no-longer-needed bone, and 2) Osteoblasts are constantly laying down new bone. In the allopathic world, MDs who see problems in bone density don't stimulate the osteoblasts through nutrition, they shut down the osteoclasts with synthetic drugs. Sure, you might see some helpful results on the tests, but now your body is accumulating the old bone cells with no way of getting rid of them. In other words, the natural process of bone regeneracy is the removal of old bone because old bones are weak. Drugs which seek to treat osteoporosis essentially fail to provide the raw materials necessary for bone growth while simultaneously shutting down the natural detoxification of old bone tissue. It is strictly speaking, a 'lose/lose' situation. The problem, as I see it, is the same problem that under-girds the entire allopathic establishment: treatment of symptoms rather than treatment of nutritional deficiencies.

Instead of getting on the allopathic train, which is a sick cycle of pain management and osteoporosis drugs, which repeats itself until one gets joint replacements, one should consider going the naturopathic route, which treats conditions through medical nutrition. Remember: the body wants to heal itself; this is simply how God designed the body to function. Rather than fight against this natural process through petroleum-derived chemicals, give the body the tools it needs to aid in its own process of healing. And what does the body need? Ninety essential nutrients! Osteoporosis, according to Dr. Glidden, is a calcium deficiency disease, plain and simple. You can't have 'too much' calcium in your diet. So, what are you waiting for?

> _**ACTION STEP**_ – Chiropractic care has been mentioned before, and it is worth repeating here. Make sure you're seeing a chiropractor, especially one well-versed in the naturopathic world. Proper nutrition is vital; chiropractic adjustments _and_ nutrition is even better!

Skin Health

Skin problems are simply nutritional deficiencies. Gluten intolerance is one of the worst culprits. Many rashes and blotches can be eliminated by getting rid of wheat, barley, rye, and in some cases oats. The reason the skin has problems is because the gut has problems. Inflammation and irritation occur (e.g., leaky gut syndrome, inflammatory bowel disease, etc.) when the body doesn't know what to do with the food—which is a sign of nutritional deficiency. Psoriasis, eczema, dermatitis, acne, rosacea, cold sores, skin tags, athlete's foot, warts, skin cancer, and other issues are a result of the intestines being inflamed and/or nutritionally deficient, and thus the skin starts to look like the gut lining.

The Mighty 90 is obviously going to be the answer for nutritional deficiencies and their accompanying illnesses and diseases. But more specifically, Dr. John Bergman recommends curcumin/turmeric for all skin disorders. Turmeric is an anti-inflammatory, antimicrobial, antioxidant that promotes healthy skin growth. Vitamin A deficiencies result in skin problems. Vitamin C deficiencies result in collagen problems. A zinc deficiency also lends itself to skin problems. Through nutritional supplementation, you can treat your body's largest organ: the skin.

When dealing with psoriasis, Dr. Axe recommends[109] five things:

1) Reduce Stress
2) Exercise and drink water
3) Apply nature-based topical remedies (Oregon grape cream, avocado and vitamin B12 cream, and aloe cream.
4) Try homeopathy and other alternative treatments (acupuncture, Chinese medicine, herbs, essential oils like tea tree, lavender, frankincense, myrrh, geranium, etc.)
5) Diet (deal with leaky gut; eat probiotic foods, high-fiber foods, foods high in antioxidants, zinc, vitamin A, herbs and spices, aloe vera).

ACTION STEP – Aside from nutrition, skin brushing can be extremely helpful. In only five minutes a day, you can dry brush your skin before a shower and rid the body of toxins, dead cells, and cellulite. Dry brushing unclogs pores and releases stress, too!

---

109 https://draxe.com/health/psoriasis-diet-5-natural-cures/

CELL BUILDING ESSENTIAL #7: HEALTHY SPIRITUAL SYSTEM

For each of the cell-building essentials we have used Dr. Tennant's illustration about rebuilding a home after a tornado strike. The same can be said of number seven: developing a healthy spiritual system. What we mean here is that your house needs a firm foundation with a fortified frame on which you can build your life. The Lord Jesus explains this principle in Matthew 7:24-27,

> Whoever hears these sayings of Mine and does them, I will liken him to a wise man who built his house on a rock. And the rain descended, the floods came, and the winds blew and beat on that house. And it did not fall, for it was founded a rock. And every one who hears these sayings of Mine and does not do them will be likened to a foolish man who built his house on the sand. And the rain descended, the floods came, and the winds blew and beat on that house. And it fell. And its fall was great.

As important as one's physiological systems are, having Christ the rock be the foundation of your life is of utmost importance. Without Christ, you're getting healthy, but to what end? Certainly not the kingdom of God on earth as it is in heaven. Because we are composed of spirit, soul, and body—as described at the outset of this chapter—we need to emphasize the thing(s) that we *don't* see, too, the other *metaphysical* things that make us human: spirit and soul. We aren't *merely* biological creatures, and we aren't *merely* spiritual creatures: we possess body, and spirit/soul. We've been put together in the image of God to have *both* physical and metaphysical natures.

The sovereign God of the universe, the maker of heaven and earth (and *you*), is the ultimate and only Great Physician, the only one who can heal the soul/spirit as well as the body. By the power of the Holy Spirit, you can be made spiritually alive, enabled by God's grace to repent of your sin and place your faith in Jesus Christ alone for salvation. Do you want to be made well? Then repent of your sins and be made well by Christ the Physician! Believe in the gospel outlined in chapter one and have the foundation necessary to experience and perpetuate the elimination of sickness and poverty in the world. It starts with *you* getting and being right with the God whose image you bear.

There is a unique connection between the physical and immaterial realm that is largely unexplored and unknown to man. What is the relationship between the emotions we experience and our physical bodies?[110] What does the anxiety we feel in our minds and hearts do to our gut lining and hormone levels? How does joy and laughter work to balance the ANS and keep our dopamine level at an appropriate place? What does sharing a healthy meal with friends and family do to our spirit as we laugh and celebrate the Lord's sabbath rest together?

We know that stress on the body through emotional anxiety can cause the ANS to be unbalanced and thus the emotion we feel affects our physical bodies in a variety of ways. When we're stressed, our digestive juices are affected and inflammation in the gut and brain starts to kick in. Inflammation isn't *inherently* bad because the body uses it to protect itself. Your physical body wants to protect and prolong itself; it wants to stay alive! But the stress we feel in the body isn't good for the long haul. While I don't want to get too far into this, I do want to simply affirm the miracle of life and that God has no doubt united the physical and metaphysical together.

For the entirety of this book we have affirmed the sovereignty of God in and over every cell, particle, and atom in the universe. This is not an accident. The Bible is the authoritative revelation of God and His plan for the world. You and I were made to reflect God's person and character: created to create, designed to design, loved in order to love. We were made from the dust, and to the dust we shall return (Gen. 3:19). In short: God demands our worship because it's the very best thing for us. We were made *by* Him *for* Him. As the Westminster Shorter Catechism teaches: What is the

---

110 See my book, *Reconstructing the Heart: Towards a Theology of Emotion* (Warrenton, VA: Cross & Crown Books, 2019).

chief end of man? Man's chief end is to glorify God and enjoy him forever.

In light of this, we ought to spend our days honoring and obeying God and His law-word. If stress is bad for the body, it's definitely bad for the soul. What are you dwelling on, Christ or your situation? Are you in prayer every day? Are you in the word of God learning and applying what God expects of you? Are you speaking to one another in "psalms, hymns, and spiritual songs," making melody in your heart to the Lord (Eph. 5:19)? Are you actively pursuing the kingdom of God with an ecclesia (church)? Are you spiritually healthy, practicing the disciplines of godliness? Is your marriage healthy? Your family? Your work/life balance?

The fact is, "Except the LORD builds the house, those who build labor in vain" (Ps. 127:1). It takes a firm foundation to uphold a home, and your life is no different. Your life, the physical and spiritual, is a house and either you are building it on the rock of Christ and His law-word, or you're building it on sinking sand. When the stress of life comes, where will you turn? When the tornado comes, will your house stand a chance? Where will you run? Your inept program of humanism?[111] If it isn't to Christ and His word, you have no fighting chance. It's either theonomy or autonomy, Christ or chaos, God's program for healing the nations, or man's program for destroying the nations.

The requirement, then, is a daily practice of Holy Spirit energy through the sowing of scriptural disciplines, a detoxing of the spiritual body through repentance, and feasting on the nutrition of God's holy word. If these things are in place, your house-life will be built on the foundation of Christ, and one thing you can count on is that His rock is *immoveable*.

---

111 See my book, *The Politics of Humanism: A Christian Response to the Humanist Worldview* (Warrenton, VA: Cross & Crown Books, 2020).

ACTION STEP – Head over to HealthForAllofLife.com and check out the recommended videos, songs, teachings, and sermons. When your mind is filled with righteousness, your life produces righteousness. The way forward is the sowing of these daily practices. Memorize your Bible using the Navigator's *Topical Memory System* (Amazon); learn to sing the Psalms; learn and sing good Christian music and hymns; and participate in the daily life of your church as you serve God and neighbor.

TEN THINGS FROM CHAPTER SIX

1) We want our bodies to be blameless before the Lord, which means we must not only *stop* the habits of sluggishness that makes us lazy, uncommitted, and generally uninterested in expending energy, and start practicing a Christianity that is fueled by passion and the physical disbursement of energy which serves the healing of the nations.

2) Neurotoxins and heavy metals through vaccines, bad food, and other toxic conditions are all things which can severely handicap the brain's functionality. When the brain's electrical currents are cut off, weakened, or deadened altogether, various health conditions exist.

3) The body has what's called an Autonomic Nervous System (ANS). 'Autonomic' refers to the involuntary, automatic system that works on autopilot.

4) In the long term, sleep deprivation debilitates us physically, mentally, emotionally, and spiritually.

5) Perhaps the most natural, inexpensive, and powerful therapy there is, grounding has been shown to: rapidly reduce inflammation, rapidly reduce chronic pain, rapidly improve blood flow, increase energy, improve sleep, and accelerate healing from injuries or surgery.

6) Blood supplies oxygen to tissues while also supplying nutrients such as glucose, amino acids, and fatty acids; it removes the waste of carbon dioxide, urea, and lactic acid; your blood provides crucial immunological functions, white blood cells, and detects foreign material by antibodies; it has the feature of coagulation, which is one part of the body's self-repair mechanism; blood contains messenger functions, transports hormones, and signals tissue damage; the blood regulates your body's pH, and regulates the core body temperature.

7) Osteoporosis, according to Dr. Glidden, is a calcium deficiency disease, plain and simple. You can't have 'too much' calcium in your diet.

8) Skin problems are simply nutritional deficiencies.

9) The Bible is the authoritative revelation of God and His plan for the world.

10) The requirement, then, is a daily practice of Holy Spirit energy through the sowing of scriptural disciplines, a detoxing of the spiritual body through repentance, and the feasting on the nutrition of God's holy word.

CONCLUSION

"Now all has been heard.
Let us hear the conclusion of the matter:
Fear God and keep His commandments,
for this is the whole duty of man."
Ecclesiastes 12:13

As I write this, we're in the midst of the 2020 coronavirus pandemic, and one thing it has proven is that the faulty postulations of the 'germ theory' have outweighed the truth of terrain theory. Virtually everyone is on the germ theory train, and I'm hoping this book will help put a stop to it. Farmer Joel Salatin explains the difference:

> In the mid-1800s Louis Pasteur peered through a microscope and saw a world of physical beings. These were not spirits; they were creatures. He did not yet know, like we do today, that they actually communicate and respond to each other. A contemporary of his named Antoine Beauchamp saw the same things. Interestingly, the two men had quite different perspectives on their new knowledge.

> Pasteur developed the germ theory and proposed ways to kill these critters. He saw nature as fundamentally flawed and in need of human intervention and fixing. It was not unlike the conclusion drawn by the Austrian chemist Justus von Liebig, who in 1837 concluded that all of life is just a rearrangement

of nitrogen, potassium, and phosphorus. This supported a mechanical view of life, that rather than being animate, life was fundamentally inanimate.

Beauchamp, however, looking at the same bacteria through the same microscopes, came to a very different conclusion from Pasteur's. He decided these new critters they were seeing under the microscope were all part of a terrain in which either wellness or sickness could thrive. He advanced the terrain theory as an alternative to Pasteur's germ theory. Generally, the populace liked the germ theory because it fit better with the notion that these devilish beings were going around making people sick. It fit well with a victim mentality, that "the devil made me sick."

Indeed, the theological portion of Pasteur's germ theory is more powerful than most people think.

Of course, we love to believe what fits with our worldview, and it was no different in that day. It was a good thing, therefore, to destroy these germs, to kill them, and thereby kill the devil's attacks on humanity. A righteous fervor propelled this idea forward. It even fit well with the "I'm not responsible" notion: "I'm not responsible for my disease; Satan through these germs is responsible. Let's knock him out."

Beauchamp had a much harder idea to sell. If these germs, most of which were actually helpful, simply changed winners and losers based on terrain, then the question to ask was this: "How do we create a terrain in which the good bugs beat the bad bugs?" He went far afield in answering this question, even looking into sleep deprivation, hygiene (imagine that, in a time when doctors were still arguing over whether it was necessary to boil surgical instruments between amputations), and food quality.

His quest for wellness-inducing terrain occupied the rest of his life. Folklore has it that Pasteur, on his deathbed, recanted and screamed: "Beauchamp was right! It is all about the terrain!" And then he died. We'll never know the definitive [sic] on this, but suffice it to say that if it's terrain, then I'm responsible. If it's germ theory, then all I have to do is figure out a concoction to kill the bad guy.[112]

What Salatin argues for is a non-mechanical, biological worldview—something I've been saying from the very beginning. The allopathic worldview which currently dominates the 'health'-care landscape is disease managing, evolutionary-centered medicine, one which treats symptoms and builds its entire 'house' on the sand of germ theory. Just this past week I was mask-shamed because I refuse to subscribe to the germ theory, but instead want my body to have a proper *terrain*, one which has a whole lot of oxygen in order to kill the bad viruses and pathogens, while giving my cells the very tool they need to do the job effectively. So no, I won't be wearing a mask, sir.

If the Church of Jesus Christ is going to have an impact on the healing of the nations—if we're going to see the elimination of poverty and sickness in the world—we must work from the terrain theory of disease and health. We must reject the Darwinian presuppositions of the natural world and instead embrace the beauty of the Creator/creature distinction of the covenant Lord of glory.

God the Creator made the world for man to dwell within, to work and keep the garden-city of God, and what God has done is given us everything we need. We don't need petroleum-based drugs which have dominated the industry for over 100 years now. We don't need BigPharma and BigGovernment ripping us off and putting their filthy hands all over the healthcare industry. We don't need a mechanistic view of man, but a biological one rooted within a theological one.

The germ theory of disease has failed over and over again, and the latest corona-crisis (there will be more) has proven this to be the case, as people have died from the coronavirus's impact on poor terrain (comorbidities). The fact that the national news hasn't covered the healing of 100 COVID patients in just 4 hours through

---

112 Salatin, Joel. *The Marvelous Pigness of Pigs* (pp. 60-61). FaithWords. Kindle Edition.

intravenous chlorine dioxide in Ecuador is proof that we've been hijacked and lied to at every turn. And yes, you should be outraged, which is what Appendix 2 will cover.

A Review

It is important to note that health is not achieved, nor disease reversed or eliminated, by practicing a fractionated approach to life. There are a variety of natural, wellness-promoting substances and protocols, but the 'silver bullet' does not exist. Understanding all of the CBEs, centered around full-spectrum nutrition, bio-electric therapies, and on-going detoxification regiments, are all involved in the process. You can visit healthforalloflife.com for the big picture.

All of the seven cell-building essentials are needed to achieve your God-glorifying health and healing goals. However, in order to aid in the memory process and to help you *do* what you now know, we'll summarize the seven CBE's into three 'Trinity Truths' to keep you in the battle of life.

Nutrify (CBE 1-2)

1. The Mighty 90 Essential Nutrients
2. Water (All Day) & CD/DMSO
3. Fulvic Acid & Nitric Oxide

Detoxify (CBE 3-4)

1. Nacent Iodine
2. Rebounding
3. Coffee Enemas & Intermittent Fasting

Energize (CBE 5-7)
1. Deep breathing exercises/aromatherapy
2. Grounding/Limiting EMF's
3. P.A.C.E. & the Word & Prayer Exercises

You are not a cosmic accident, and your ancestors never crawled out of the primordial goo. God has made your body and soul with intelligence, which means 1) It *knows* how to heal itself; 2) It *wants* to heal itself; and 3) It *can* heal itself, when supplied with God's natural and supernatural fuel and fire.

In order to get healthy and stay healthy, you have to have a strong immune system, which fights off the bad and promotes the good. *Food is everything.* You can exercise as a full-time job and go eat McDonald's (people do this) and *not* be healthy. Nutrition is absolutely the name of the game. Nutrition is what heals the gut, nutrition is what builds your cells, and nutrition is what gives your body the fuel it needs to correct any wayward conditions. So, eat clean!

This author eats a whole-foods, plant-based diet with plenty of fiber, and plenty of nutrition in the day-to-day. While I do recommend this way of eating (See *The China Study* for my reasons), the key is making sure to eat good foods and avoid the nutrient-deficient foods.

Remember: *you're not sick because you lack drugs, you're sick because you lack nutrition and cellular voltage.* No one has a cold because the body is short on antibiotics.

I hope and pray that this manifesto would serve to impact the world for good. If there was ever a time for the Church of King Jesus to stand up and offer the world a better blueprint for health and healing, that time is right now. Do not let this information die—be a conduit by giving people more Vitamin-I!

And remember the call of Proverbs 3:1-8,

My son, do not forget my teaching,
　　but let your heart keep my commandments;
for length of days and long life
　　and peace will they add to you.

Do not let mercy and truth forsake you;
　　bind them around your neck,
　　write them on the tablet of your heart,
so you will find favor and good understanding
　　in the sight of God and man.

Trust in the Lord with all your heart,
and lean not on your own understanding;
in all your ways acknowledge Him,
and He will direct your paths.

Do not be wise in your own eyes;
fear the Lord and depart from evil.
It will be health to your body,
and strength to your bones.

APPENDIX 1

The Poor Man's Medicine Cabinet

The following suggestions are placed here to give you concise and convenient access to wonderful resources. Most are things that my family and I have used and are using; others are there because they fit within the worldview I am espousing. They are organized into various categories, making them easier to find. Caution: in no possible way can I endorse every single thing, for some of the authors listed below would not align with the biblical worldview I have laid out in this book. Many are Christians, some are not, so keep that in mind.

Medicine & Health Books:

- **Healing is Voltage: The Handbook** by Jerry Tennant
- **Epigenetics: The Death of the Genetic Theory of Disease Transmission** by Joel Wallach, et al.
- **Dead Doctors Don't Lie** by Joel Wallach
- **The Truth about Nutrition** by Joel Wallach
- **Cancer is Not Genetic** by John Bergman

- **Everybody is Sick and I Know Why** by Peter Glidden
- **MMS Health Recovery Guidebook** by Jim Humble
- **The DMSO Handbook for Doctors** by Archie H. Scott
- **The Truth About Cancer** by Ty M. Bollinger (Also a DVD series)
- **Chris Beat Cancer** by Chris Wark
- **Feeding You Lies: How to Unravel the Food Industry's Playbook and Reclaim Your Health** by Vani Hari
- **The Marvelous Pigness of Pigs** by Joel Salatin
- **Folks, This Ain't Normal** by Joel Salatin
- **The Cure is in the Cupboard: How to Use Wild Oregano for Better Health** by Cass Ingram
- **P.A.C.E.: The 12-Minute Fitness Revolution** by Al Sears
- **The China Study** by T. Colin Campbell & Thomas M. Campbell II
- **Unlock the Power to Heal** by Robert Scott Bell & Ty M. Bollinger
- **Regenerate** by Sayer Ji
- **Cancer and the New Biology of Water** by Thomas Cowan
- **Fiber Fueled** by Will Bulsiewicz
- **Alternative First Aid Reference Guide** by Kerri Rivera & John Thomas
- **Dissolving Illusions** by Suzanne Humphries & Roman Bystrianyk
- **Callous Disregard** by Andrew J. Wakefield
- **Vaccines: A Reappraisal** by Richard Moskowitz
- **Vaccines, Autoimmunity, and the Changing Nature of Childhood Illness** by Thomas Cowan
- **The Earth Prescription** by Laura Koniver
- **Stop Fighting Cancer and Start Treating the Cause** by Kevin Conners
- **Murder by Injection** by Eustace Clarence Mullins

- **How to Raise a Healthy Child in Spite of Your Doctor** by Robert S. Mendelsohn
- **Confessions of a Medical Heretic** by Robert S. Mendelsohn
- **Racketerring in Medicine** by James P. Cater
- **Enzyme Nutrition** by Edward Howell
- **Every Woman's Book** by Paavo Airola

Books for the Soul and for Battle:

- **Reconstructing the Heart: Towards a Theology of Emotion** by Jason Garwood
- **The Politics of Humanism: A Christian Response to the Humanist Worldview** by Jason Garwood
- **A Body of Divinity** by Thomas Watson
- **Knowing God** by J.I. Packer
- **Truth and Transformation: A Manifesto for Ailing Nations** by Vishal Mangalwadi
- **The Institutes of Biblical Law** by R.J. Rushdoony
- **Revolt Against Maturity** by R.J. Rushdoony
- **Church Shift** by Sunday Adeleja

DVD's & Videos (Most are linked on the *Health for all of Life* website):

- **The Truth About Cancer**
- **The Truth About Vaccines**
- **Bio-Slugged** (YouTube Documentary)
- **Game Changers** (Netflix Documentary)

Nutrition:

- **Youngevity's** '90 for Life' supplements[113]

---

113 https://drjasongarwood.youngevity.com

- **Garden of Life's** *mykind* organic supplements[114]
- Organic raw/whole foods!
- Femallay Organic Teas[115]

Misc. Protocols & Products:

- **Advanced TRS** (Toxic Removal System) for detoxing heavy metals.[116]
- Organic **BioCare CBD** oil[117]
- CD/MMS and DMSO[118]
- EMF protection tools like grounding mats and router sleeves[119]
- Organic Essential Oils (döTERRA or Young Living)
- Anything and everything from Barlow Herbal[120]

Websites:

- www.healthforalloflife.com
- www.greenmedinfo.com
- www.naturalnews.com
- www.criticalhealthnews.com
- www.nutritionfacts.org
- www.tennantinstitute.com
- www.kerririvera.com
- www.draxe.com
- www.glidden.healthcare
- www.bergmanchiropractic.com
- www.chrisbeatcancer.com
- www.drjaydavidson.com

---

114 https://www.gardenoflife.com
115 https://www.femallay.com
116 http://bit.ly/JasonCoseva
117 http://bit.ly/MaryCBDOil
118 https://kvlab.com
119 https://www.earthing.com
120 https://barlowherbal.com

- www.alsearsmd.com
- www.drsuzanne.net
- www.intuition-physician.com
- www.AndrewKaufmanMD.com
- www.ConnersClinic.com
- www.thehighwire.com
- www.ise.media
- www.nutritionstudies.org
- www.microbeformulas.com
- www.naturessunshine.com
- www.speroprotectionclothing.com
- www.earthing.com
- www.drjasongarwood.youngevity.com
- www.drjasongarwood.cosevatrs.com
- www.bit.ly/MaryCBDOil
- www.JasonGarwood.com

APPENDIX 2

Resisting State-Controlled Medicine

W hile taking a stroll through my local grocery store, I unwittingly, albeit necessarily, passed by the pharmacy only to be confronted with a sign which read, "Vaccine season is back! Get your vaccine today and help save lives." What an interesting thing to say. First, there's a season now? I mean, we've all become accustomed to flu season, and methinks corona-season will be a thing now too, but 'vaccine season'? *Something's afoot.* Second, how does this 'save' lives? Are you suggesting that lives are worth saving (I agree!)? If so, why would you put it next to something so deadly as vaccination? You don't *really* mean this. After all, vaccines cause autism, and frankly, the last thing anyone needs are regular injections of aborted fetal cell DNA proteins—again, *lives* matter, right? Speaking of the preborn, do you, grocery-store-people-who-inject-poison, want to save *those* lives, too? *Hardly.*

The propaganda is everywhere, especially during the current coronavirus pandemic. Signs are hoisted and splattered on the front doors of businesses. Commercials pop up on television, our Facebook newsfeeds, and burst through the speakers of our stores.

The cool thing to do right now as a celebrity, besides participate in pedophilia schemes (may God judge swiftly), is to snap a selfie of your righteous mask-wearing in order to use your platform to demonstrate your empty-headedness. Christians love to fly overseas to snap selfies of little African kids; Hollywood does the same thing with their masks. *How cute.*

Right now, many states have chosen to mandate masks, even encouraging you to snitch on your neighbor and his business if he doesn't comply. In Michigan you can receive a $500 fine (tax) for refusing to wear a mask. Aside from the fact that masks severely handicap one of your body's most important detoxification functions (breathing is essential!), they don't actually work anyway (looking at you Mr. Sneaky Handkerchief Wearer). Besides, when did the civil magistrate obtain permission to mandate such nonsense anyway?

Here's my argument: *it's not about science, it's about control.* If you look at the title of this appendix you could basically interchange the word "medicine" with a whole host of other things. It could say, "Resisting State-Controlled Schools," or "Resisting State-Controlled Licensing." Truth be told, there's a whole lot of things we could say about a whole lot of state-controlled problems. The difficult pill to swallow lies in the fact that our governments control just about every single aspect of life, many things of which ought to be left to individual judgment and localities. If I want to build a deck (join me for a fun little thought experiment), why do I need a permit? If I do a terrible job and someone gets hurt, then I am liable. To say the obvious: the state does not have the ability to stand on my deck. I don't invite the 'state' to come hang out at my house while we barbeque and eat cantaloupe. If I can't have a cookout with the state, how in the world could they possible be a victim to my 'negligence'? They can't: hence the problem.[121]

The problem with state-controlled anything is twofold: 1) The Bible tells us in Romans 13 that the civil magistrate, which is a lawful office, is for the sole purpose of punishing evil and rewarding

---

121 See my book, *The Politics of Humanism* for more absurdities.

good; and 2) The state is a terrible savior which inherently means that it is a terrible planner and executer as well. Any time central planners try to do anything, it inevitably costs more, takes more time, and the quality is much, much lower. The reason this is the case is because central planners are too far removed from its citizens. Anthony Esolen writes about the principle of subsidiarity...

> [T]he principle states that social concerns should be left to the smallest group that can reasonably deal with them, the group that is nearest to the concerns in question. If the family can deal with it, then it is not the problem of the neighborhood; if the neighborhood, then it is not the problem of the village; if the village, then it is not the problem of the county; if the county, then not the state; if the state, then not the nation. We do not want a national committee to send official Diaper Changers to every home with a little baby in it. Nor do we want a state committee to send official Book Orderers to every school with an English teacher in it.[122]

Could you imagine Diaper Changers being dispatched to homes with newborn babies in them? You may well laugh, because the process of diaper changing isn't really difficult, but given our penchant for wanting someone else to do our own self-government for us, I'm sure it could happen. But 'diaper' changing—follow me here—happens all of the time *because the state has become a bloated nanny who's too drunk on power to know when to stop.* The more we give, the more she takes, and she's never satisfied. And when does it stop? And how do we know where to draw that line?

Esolen's description is essentially biblical law in action. Certain categories of society belong to certain segments of society. The family is in charge of education, and if a particular family wants to appeal to a free market for education materials, tutoring, etc., then they should be able to do so without being held at gun point to

---

122 Esolen, Anthony. *Out of the Ashes: Rebuilding American Culture* (p. 174). Regnery Publishing. Kindle Edition.

pay a compulsory property tax. An individual should be trusted to take care of himself without coercive doctors being controlled by coercive pharmaceutical companies.

To put it another way, the issue of health and wellness, which has been a complete disaster ever since the Flexner Report, belongs to free individuals forming free market enterprises without a bunch of slimy red tape getting in the way. According to healthsystemtracker.org, "Health spending totaled $74.6 billion in 1970. By 2000, health expenditures had reached about $1.4 trillion, and in 2018 the amount spent on health had more than doubled to $3.6 trillion."[123] The fact that healthcare has risen to this height ought to make us pause and wonder where the problem lies. Since BigGovernment has a chokehold on just about everything, and because it has a superiority complex, our political leaders think that the answer is more red tape, more control, and more regulations. This unintended consequence is its own doing: the more government gets involved, the worse it gets. Why? Because *political leaders can't collectively do what free individuals in free markets can do.*

Free men, when unmolested by government agents, will always create and innovate far more technology for far less money than any government committee could ever dream. This is because God gives us both the freedom and the dominion mandate to carry forth biblical progress into the world.

In order for us to move forward we have to quit taking the government cheese. As much as possible, we have to get the nanny away from us and this will only happen when we starve her. Don't take the unemployment (the Church should be there to help). Don't take the food stamps (again, the Church ought to be there). Do whatever you can wherever you can to stay away from the MDs who are nothing but political pawns in the hands of the wealthy elite. Get your kids out of government schools immediately. Don't get vaccines, don't go to the hospital (unless it's a true emergency),

---

123 https://www.healthsystemtracker.org/chart-collection/u-s-spending-healthcare-changed-time/#item-nhe-trends_total-national-health-expenditures-us-billions-1970-2018

and by all means never, ever assume that a medical 'professional' knows best.

We are sadly living in an age of medical tyranny. Medical kidnapping is a real thing. Forced vaccination is a real thing. They have mandated masks: don't think for one second that they won't try and mandate other things. You need to have a game plan, and you need one yesterday. Let me offer some things.

First, you need legal counsel. I recommend familiarizing yourself with two organizations: 1) Children's Health Defense;[124] and 2) Heritage Defense.[125] Regarding the first organization, which is led by Robert F. Kennedy, Jr., their mission is "to end the childhood health epidemics by working aggressively to eliminate harmful exposures, hold those responsible accountable, and establish safeguards so this never happens again." RFK Jr. has been instrumental in helping provide legal counsel for children and families who have suffered under the boot of medical tyranny. Regarding the second organization, Heritage Defense, their mission is to "defend the God-given parental rights of Christian, homeschooling families." Both organizations are worth your time and investment. Don't wait until it's too late to deal with a situation. Educate yourself and plan accordingly (Luke 14:28).

Second, localism is where it's at. One thing we have done locally is agitate our local sheriff and county board of supervisors. It is imperative that they hear from you. Attend meetings, voice your concerns about medical tyranny, and implore them to resist state-controlled medicine. Yes, you might be dubbed a crazy person, but this is only because they have, by and large, stuck their necks in the sand. Don't let them do that. If we're going to advance the cause of Christ's kingdom, particularly the freedom and liberty that he gives individuals, then you're simply going to have to fight.

Third, utilizing such tools as Facebook, Instagram, and other social media platforms, get connected with other like-minded medical-freedom lovers. Trust me, they're out there. I've met them.

---

124 https://childrenshealthdefense.org
125 https://heritagedefense.org

Here in Virginia, we have a couple of different groups that are full of men and women who persistently lobby state representatives, senators, and governors. Let me warn you up front: it's exhausting and demanding. I jokingly told some of our church members one day, "Being an activist and defending basic liberties is a full-time job!" Going to local board meetings, attending rallies and lobbyist events, and generally staying in the loop so as to keep an eye on your elected officials, you will at times feel hopeless and out of energy. *Don't give up.* The snowball that has been our bloated central government will never, ever stop itself. Which means we need to be the ones to stand in its path.

Lastly, you're going to need to wake up the sleepy Church. Pastors are going to need to preach on some difficult topics. The reason—let me be a little aggressive here—that they *don't* preach on these things is because they don't know anything about it. Seminary never taught them, and the people of God don't demand much of them. Far too many Christians are functional pietists[126] who would rather sit around the slowly dwindling campfire and wait to be zapped off the planet (which will never actually happen anyway).

If you're in a church and there has been no game plan to deal with the problem of statism in general, and medical tyranny in particular, then start sounding the alarm. I know who you are. I've talked to you. You're trying and they *just won't listen.* Keep trying and try some more. Or perhaps, if the Lord allows, you should move to a local assembly that *does* preach about these things.

We need to fight back, and we need to do it now. My prayer is that these principles will help you navigate the murky waters so as to promote change in the world, the type of change that loves God and neighbor, and does not give tyranny a foothold.

---

126 https://jasongarwood.com/the-problem-of-pietism/

APPENDIX 3

Meet The Faculty

Since *HealthForAllOfLife.com* is meant to be an online medical center—a bootcamp no less—I thought it important to highlight the many men and women introduced to you throughout this book. They are also our 'resident scholars' who are there on the website teaching you how to heal your own body so that the nations can be healed. Below you will find their picture and their biography. I encourage you to learn from them. Buy their books, visit their websites listed in Appendix 1, and pray that God would use them mightily for the Kingdom.

Kerri Rivera is an author, speaker, health consultant and autism mom. She has helped over 800 kids (ages 6 months – 32 years old) recover from autism. After her son was diagnosed with autism in 2004, she began treating him with the standard DAN biomedical interventions popular at the time. He was a "non-responder" and after years of treatment his results were disappointing.

In desperation, she prayed for a solution to her son's health problems. Asking God to help her find something that would help her son and that she could share with others; a solution that would be affordable and accessible around the world and effective in relieving the autism symptoms affecting an increasing number of the world's youth.

Finding Chlorine Dioxide shortly thereafter, she tried it on herself and with her son. He had an immediate and obvious improvement in symptoms. The veil of autism was lifted and he began speaking in ways he hadn't for years. Kerri knew she was on to something and began to share her discovery with the world.

In 2014 Kerri's Book, *Healing The Symptoms Known As Autism*, was published on Amazon, becoming a #1 Best Seller in the Health category before being banned in 2019 when Amazon began a dramatic purge of literature focusing on natural health. The book itself, translated into seven languages is filled with testimonials from happy families and racked up scores of additional positive online reviews from people who had never met Kerri, but were benefiting from her protocol as spelled out in the book.

To support her growing following, Kerri created Facebook groups that attracted fans from around the world. In addition to English- and Spanish-speaking groups (Kerri is bilingual), parents offered to help moderate groups in Arabic (10K members), Turkish (12K members) and Portuguese. Before being banned by

Facebook in another drastic social media censorship sweep, Kerri's groups had between 50,000 and 100,000 followers.

Due to privacy concerns on social media, Kerri has now converted to meeting with families via an inexpensive paid membership group here: https://www.kerririveraprotocol.com/home-page

Through working with the FAMILIES of her autistic clients, Kerri has seen dramatic improvements in health of individuals struggling with a variety of health concerns, not just autism. Her protocols are wondrously effective in treating even chronic diseases.

As a result, Kerri has published a new book, with broader appeal. Her latest book, *Alternative First Aid Reference Guide for Campers, Preppers and Household Use,* has just been released! You can get your first-run copy here: www.kerririvera.com/

This book is designed to help you use the safe, natural products we recommend for a variety of every-day health conditions.

Jerry Tennant, MD, MD(H), PScD, founder of The Tennant Institute for Integrative Medicine and Senergy Medical Group, is a world-renowned physician and integrative health practitioner.

Dr. Jerry Tennant is a true Renaissance man. He is a teacher, inventor, healer, scholar, humanitarian, innovator, and entrepreneur — those are just a few of the ways we describe Dr. Tennant who has led a remarkable life dedicated to healing and innovation, which has altered the paradigm of western medicine. People from around the world travel to the Tennant Institute for Integrative Medicine in Colleyville, Texas, to seek out and benefit from his healing expertise.

Through his *Tennant Principles*, Dr. Tennant's mission is to inform patients and practitioners how the body requires voltage to make new cells in order to maintain health and wellness, as well as incorporate traditional medicine with integrative medicine for better results.

He is also the author of *Healing is Voltage® The Handbook, Healing is Voltage® Textbook, Healing is Voltage® Healing Eye Diseases, Acupuncture Muscle Batteries, Healing is Voltage®,* and *Cancer's On/ Off Switches: Polarity.* These books are based on his own personal experience and continuous energetic medical research.

• •

Peter Glidden, BS. ND.
▪ Naturopathic physician with over 30 years of clinical experience
▪ Mentored under the legendary Dr. Joel Wallach (of *Dead Doctors Don't Lie* fame) for over 4 years
▪ Host of Health Talk/YouTube channel
▪ Dedicated to public education, he also delivers 40+ free international health lectures a year
▪   Authored "Everybody Is Sick and I Know Why" an eye-opening, groundbreaking, jaw dropping exposition on the shortcomings of conventional M.D.- directed medicine and the unrivaled excellence of Wholistic medical treatments

Chris Wark is an author, speaker and health coach. He was diagnosed with stage 3 colon cancer in 2003 at 26 years old. He had surgery, but instead of chemotherapy used nutrition and natural therapies to heal himself. Chris has lectured at smoothie bars, health and wellness events, hospitals, churches, culinary schools, Whole Foods Market and more. Chris has made many appearances on radio and television including The Ricki Lake Show and The Lisa Oz Show, he was also featured in *The Truth About Cancer* docuseries and in the award-winning documentary film The C Word. Chris inspires countless people to take control of their health and reverse disease with a radical transformation of diet and lifestyle.

Joel D. Wallach is a veterinarian, naturopathic physician, author and lecturer who played a major role in the development of the market of liquid vitamin – mineral supplements. He became nationally known through his widely distributed audio tape, "Dead Doctors Don't Lie." Periodically, critics question his background and some of his views. The present account specifically analyzes some of the objections raised in the Third Edition of the Medical Resource Manual (First Image, Inc.), 1997 pp. 74-75.

Joel D. Wallach was born in West St. Louis County on June 4, 1940. Growing up on a farm led him to decide already early in his life to become a veterinarian and nutritionist. After finishing high school, Wallach enrolled in the University of Missouri at Columbia, first to study Agriculture with a major in animal husbandry and a minor in field crops and soils. The School of Agriculture at the University of Missouri has departments of nutrition, food science, geology and biochemistry and an internationally acclaimed "Trace Substances Research Center" which explores the biological, economic, and health significance of trace substances in environmental health. In this interdisciplinary academic environment, Wallach flourished and gathered a wealth of information that would later help him in his practice as a veterinary pathologist and naturopathic physician. In 1962, Wallach received a B.S. Degree in Agriculture from Missouri and continued on to study veterinary medicine at the same Institution, which in 1964 awarded him the degree of Doctor of Veterinary Medicine (D.V.M.). From 1966 to 1967, he held a post-doctoral fellowship in comparative medicine at the Center for the Biology of Natural Systems, George-Washington-University, St. Louis. Thereafter, Wallach worked at Iowa State University Diagnostic Laboratory, Ames, Iowa, and subsequently, for two years, at Natal Fish & Game Department, Natal, Republic of South Africa.

John Bergman, D.C., was propelled into chiropractic by a severe auto accident, with two broken legs, fractured skull, and sternum, along with several organ injuries. With the great need and a passion for healing and regenerating, Dr. Bergman began studying the body's recovery process. Dr. Bergman obtained his degree in Doctor of Chiropractic at Cleveland Chiropractic College in Los Angeles (CCCLA), California.

Dr. Bergman's teaching at CCCLA: Human Anatomy, Physiology, Biomechanics, and four chiropractic techniques: Full Spine Specific (Palmer Method), Thompson, Diversified, and Extremity Adjusting. As a past instructor, Dr. Bergman has extensive knowledge of human anatomy and human physiology that few can match.

Dr. Bergman's practice has continued to grow serving hundreds of families, focusing on corrective and wellness care and is dedicated to pediatric development and adult health care. With Dr. Bergman's unique approach and direct experience of recovery from a severe injury, many successes can be achieved even with the most challenging cases.

In his spare time, he enjoys sailing, biking, camping, and spending time with his two sons Michael and Danny. Dr. Bergman has been serving Huntington Beach and its surrounding communities since May 1998. Dr. Bergman was born and raised in Burbank, CA. After graduating at 16 years old from John Burroughs High School, he did his prerequisite studies in Santa Barbara, California.

Natural Pharmacist **Benjamin Fuchs** is a registered pharmacist, nutritionist and cosmetic chemist.

Benjamin Fuchs holds a B.A. in Broadcast Journalism from Syracuse University and B.S. in Pharmacy from the University of Colorado and has practiced as a Registered Pharmacist and Consulting Nutritionist for over 15 years.

Mr. Fuchs has been compounding custom medication, formulating nutritional products and consulting with doctors and patients since graduating from the University of Colorado School of Pharmacy in 1986. Since 1991 has been lecturing nationwide on the importance of the strategic use of cosmetics and nutritional supplementation for healthy skin and bodies.

Youngevity Scientific Advisory Board Member, January 27th 2013. The Youngevity Scientific Advisory Board comprises some of the most respected names in the fields of medicine, research, and nutrition. Working together with our Founder, Dr. Joel Wallach, DVM, ND, the Scientific Advisory Board's collective guidance is practical, insightful, and often based on individual member's own pioneering research.

"Pharmacist Ben", host of *The Bright Side*, a nationally syndicated radio program on the Genesis Communications Radio Network.

Dr. Josh Axe, D.C., D.N.M., C.N.S., is a Doctor of Chiropractic, certified doctor of natural medicine, and a clinical nutritionist with a passion to help people eat healthy and live a healthy lifestyle. In 2008, he started a functional medicine center in Nashville, which grew to become one of the most renowned clinics in the world.

Dr. Axe founded the website **DrAxe.com**, which is one the top natural health websites in the world today. Its main topics include nutrition, natural medicine, fitness, healthy recipes, home DIY remedies, and trending health news. His website includes a group of credentialed editors, writers, and a Medical Review Board.

He has also been a resource for many professional athletes. In 2009, he began working with the Wellness Advisory Council and Professional Swim Teams. He worked with professional swimmers, providing nutritional advice and performing musculoskeletal work on the athletes to increase their performance. He also traveled to the 2012 Games in London to work with USA athletes.

Dr. Josh Axe has authored several celebrated and bestselling books including *Eat Dirt*, *The Real Food Diet Cookbook* and *Essential Oils Ancient Medicine*. *Eat Dirt: Why Leaky Gut May Be the Root Cause of Your Health Problems and 5 Surprising Steps to Cure It* was published by Harper New Wave in March 2016, and it currently receives 4.6 out of 5 stars on Amazon. In January 2017, *Essential Oils: Ancient Medicine for the Modern World* was published, and it's garnered 4.7 out of 5 stars on Amazon. On February 19, 2019, Little Brown & Company will publish *Keto Diet: Your 30-Day Plan to Lose Weight, Balance Hormones, and Reverse Disease*, and it promises to be the definitive book on the ketogenic diet.

Millions of people have read his books and gone through his programs, including Healing Leaky Gut and Essential Oils

Transformation. These books and programs combine the power of advanced nutrition with recipes, herbal remedies and lifestyle improvements to help people reach their health goals.

. . . .

Ty Bollinger is a happily married husband and father, Christian, health freedom advocate, health researcher, former competitive bodybuilder, talk radio host, documentary film producer, and best-selling author. After losing several family members to cancer (including his mother and father), Ty refused to accept the notion that chemotherapy, radiation, and surgery were the most effective treatments available for cancer patients.

He began a quest to learn all he possibly could about alternative cancer treatments and the medical industry. What he uncovered was shocking. There is ample evidence to support the allegation that the "war on cancer" is largely a fraud and that multinational pharmaceutical companies are "running the show."

In 2006, after almost a decade of cancer research, and in an effort to spread the truth to the world, he published Cancer – Step Outside the Box which (now in its 6th edition) has become a bestseller (over 150,000 copies sold) and has been called the "most eye-opening book since 1984." He is the author of several other books, including Monumental Myths, A Guide to Understanding Herbal Medicine, and Unlock the Power to Heal. On October 25, 2016, Ty released The Truth About Cancer (book) which hit #2 on the New York Times bestseller list the first week it was released and stayed in the top 10 for 12 weeks.

Along with his wife, Charlene, Ty is co-founder of "The Truth About Cancer" and has produced several documentary mini-series (docu-series) including:

- *The Quest for The Cures* ™

- *The Quest for The Cures* ™
- *The Truth About Cancer: A Global Quest* ™
- *The Truth About Detox* ™
- *The Truth About Vaccines* ™
- *The Truth About Pet Cancer* ™

In total, these documentary films have been viewed by over 20 million people worldwide.

Ty speaks frequently at seminars, expos, conferences, churches, and is a regular guest on multiple radio shows and writes for numerous magazines and websites. He has appeared numerous times on FOX News, multiple documentary films, and he co-hosts a weekly radio show.

His message is that cancer is not a death sentence. There is always hope.

• •

Charlene Bollinger is a devoted Christian, happily married wife, joyful mother of 4 beautiful home educated children, health freedom advocate, former model/actress/fitness buff, and lover of healthy food and healthy living.

After losing various family members to conventional cancer treatments, she and her husband, Ty, learned the truth about cancer and the cancer industry. After losing Ty's mom (her Mother-in-Love) she made it her life's mission to save other lives and families from being plundered by doing all she could to reach the world with the truth: cancer does NOT have to be a death sentence. So she and Ty set out on a quest to compile as much information together and get it to everyone in the world so that they could live and long, vibrant, happy life.

Charlene is now CEO of The Truth About Cancer and The Truth About Vaccines films and she is also CEO and President of the United

Medical Freedom Super PAC (UMFSP). Charlene has a series of YouTube interviews she has done on The Truth About COVID and Censorship on her YouTube channel and has produced the virtual Pandemic Town Halls through the UMFSP featuring a panel of doctors sharing natural protocols for COVID.

Charlene speaks at various conferences and is a guest on various health related radio shows together with Ty, helping people to learn that cancer does NOT have to be a death sentence. Together they host a biweekly internet news show program, TTAC Global Health News.

She believes and advocates that cancer does not have to be a death sentence. As long as there's breath, there's hope. She is fearless and believes, as Ronald Reagen said, "Evil is powerless when the good are unafraid." She continues to do all she can with the many gifts God has given to push back tyranny and help America return to her God given roots so that we will once again honor God and enjoy the freedom He gave to us to do so.

· ·

Al Sears, M.D. is America's #1 anti-aging doctor. He's made it his life's work to challenge conventional medical beliefs and bring his patients the latest breakthroughs in natural cures and remedies to diseases once thought to be "incurable."

Dr. Sears takes a fresh, novel approach to patient health and wellness. Our environment and food supply have changed for the worse — and it's affecting your health. He helps patients return to their "Native Health" and escape accelerated aging caused by modern toxins, pollutants, preservatives, chemicals and other hormonal threats you unknowingly face every day.

Every year, he travels over 20,000 miles to the most remote regions of the world searching for natural healing secrets unknown or ignored by mainstream medicine. Since 1999, Dr. Sears has published 35 books and reports on health and wellness. He has millions of loyal readers spread over 163 countries.

Today he writes and publishes two monthly e-Newsletters, *Confidential Cures and Anti-Aging Confidential for Women*, and a daily email broadcast, *Doctor's House Call*, with more than 500,000 sub-scribers. He has also appeared on more than 50 national radio pro-grams, ABC News, CNN and ESPN.

Dr. Sears was one of the first to be board-certified by the American Academy of Anti-Aging Medicine (A4M). More than 25,000 patients travel from all around the world to visit him at the Sears Institute for Anti-Aging Medicine in beautiful Royal Palm Beach, Florida.

Dr. Sears first created waves in the medical community when he spoke out against conventional beliefs about heart disease. His book *The Doctor's Heart Cure* created an easy-to-follow solution that eliminates your risk of heart attack, high blood pressure, and stroke without taking statins or eating a low-fat diet.

He went on to shock the fitness world by revealing the dan-gers of "cardio" exercise. His fast, simple solution restores muscle strength, guards against heart attack, and burns excess fat. Today, his revolutionary PACE exercise program is practiced by thousands of people worldwide.

And recently, Dr. Sears proved you can affect the way you age by controlling the length of your telomeres. He made history as the first M.D. to introduce the Nobel prize-winning, anti-aging break-through of our time, telomere DNA therapy, to the general public. And now he's working with the leading scientists in the field of telomere biology to further define how this incredible technology will shape the future of anti-aging medicine.

David Jockers D.N.M., D.C., M.S. is a doctor of natural medicine, functional nutritionist, and corrective care chiropractor. He is the founder of Exodus Health Center in Kennesaw, Georgia and DrJockers.com, a website designed to empower people with science-based solutions to improve their health.

DrJockers.com has gotten over 1 million monthly page views and is considered one of the most well-researched and easy-to-read health websites in the world. Dr Jockers work has been published in various popular media outlets including ABC, Fox News, The Hallmark Channel – Home and Family and the Dr Oz Show.

He has developed several revolutionary online programs with thousands of participants. These programs include E-guides, recipe guides, meal plans and video instructions including "The Fasting Transformation Quickstart Program," "The Sugar Detox," "Navigating the Ketogenic Diet," "The Digestive Health Restoration Program," and the "Super Brain Program."

Dr Jockers is a sought-after speaker around the country on such topics as weight loss, brain health, functional exercise, natural detoxification, and disease prevention. Dr Jockers sees patients from all over the world at his clinic, Exodus Health Center, where he helps customize specific lifestyle plans to improve performance and live with less pain and more energy.

His new book, *The Keto Metabolic Breakthrough* was published by Victory Belt in January 2020 and can be found online and in bookstores everywhere. Dr Jockers also hosts the popular Dr Jockers Functional Nutrition podcast.

Laura Koniver, M.D., received her medical doctorate degree from Jefferson Medical College in 2000 at the age of twenty-six, and has been passionately supporting her patients' natural healing ever since. She is an artist, author, holistic physician, and internationally recognized grounding advocate. Koniver's healing artwork has been featured in many news and media outlets, and she's published her own children's book on grounding, *From the Ground Up*. She writes a regular health column in the national organic lifestyle magazine, *MaryJanesFarm*; is featured as an expert protagonist in several motion pictures, including *The Grounded, Heal for Free, The Earthing Movie*, and *Down to Earth*; and runs the popular health care blog, www.intuition-physician.com, where she reviews medical literature in a holistic and intuitive way.

Mike Adams, the "Health Ranger," is an outspoken consumer health advocate, award-winning investigative journalist, internet activist and science lab director.

He is the founder and editor of NaturalNews.com, the internet's most-trafficked natural health news website.

Adams has received accolades and testimonials from several key influencers in the natural health space, including Dr. Michael T. Murray and raw food pioneer David Wolfe.

Mike Adams is widely recognized as having a strong technical aptitude that has allowed his websites to achieve very high degrees of success on the internet. He is also widely known to be a highly influential writer and presenter.

• •

Del Bigtree is one of the preeminent voices of the vaccine risk awareness movement around the world. He is the founder of the non-profit, Informed Consent Action Network, and host of a rapidly growing internet talk show The HighWire, boasting over 33 million views to date. Del's multi-pronged approach incorporates legal, legislative, and media actions to expose the fraud, lies, and conflicts of interest that have allowed the pharmaceutical industry to evade standardized safety testing for vaccines. This collusion between government agencies and the pharmaceutical industry, now the most powerful lobby in Washington, has led to a dramatic increase in vaccine injuries, estimated to be as high as 5.9 million cases per year in the US alone. Despite mainstream media sources such as the New York Times and Washington Post blame so-called "Anti-Vaxxers" for the growing trend of vaccine hesitancy, Del has focused the spotlight on the real issue – the shocking lack of credible vaccine science.

Del's foray into the vaccine issue was anything but intentional. After spending a decade celebrating great doctors, cutting edge surgeries and medical breakthroughs as a producer on The Dr. Phil Show and the CBS medical talk show, The Doctors, it was a routine investigation into the story of a whistleblower at the Centers for Disease Control and Prevention (CDC) that catapulted Del into the vaccine debate. When every news agency in television, including The Doctors, refused to cover the story of Dr. William Thompson, a senior scientist at the CDC who had provided over 10,000 documents to support his claim that the agency had destroyed scientific evidence proving a connection between vaccines and autism, Del put his career on the line and left network television to make one of the most controversial documentaries in history: Vaxxed: From Cover-Up To Catastrophe. The film became a worldwide phenomenon when it was abruptly removed from the 2016 Tribeca Film Festival lineup under unprecedented pressure by the festival's medical sponsor, The Sloan Foundation.

Del is now one of the most sought-after public speakers in the natural health arena, often gathering audiences in the thousands who travel from around the world to be inspired by his unique blend of passion, wit, and scientific expertise. He has worked directly with the likes of Robert Kennedy Jr., Robert DeNiro, and Jenny McCarthy, and was an official member of the 2017 Kennedy Vaccine Safety Delegation at the National Institute of Health arranged by President Trump. He is the recipient of multiple awards including an Emmy Award as a producer on The Doctors, Best Drama at the New York Television Festival, and the Health Freedom Hero Award from the National Health Freedom Federation, the oldest natural health organization in America. He has appeared on several primetime news networks including ABC, NBC, CBS, and FOX and has been interviewed by countless radio and Internet personalities ranging from Tom Hartman to David Knight of Infowars. Above all, Del is most fulfilled by his work with the brave mothers and fathers of vaccine injured children who are marching on state capitols around the nation to stop Big Pharma's push to forcibly inject every American citizen with vaccines, a product the Supreme Court has described as "unavoidably unsafe."

APPENDIX 4

What Is Humanism?

There is only one rival worldview and religion to the Christian faith, and its history dates back to the dawn of creation. This religion can aptly be called (and indeed it should be called) *humanism*.

Humanism, as the name implies, emphasizes the centrality of man in every area of life: his reason, his ethical nature, his purpose. It is an *ism* which suggests that it is much more than one particular dogma or tenet. In a most basic definition, humanism is the result of man throwing off his responsibility and accountability to God. We call this autonomy (self-law). Made in God's image, Adam and Eve were decidedly against doing things God's way, so they chose their own way, and as a result, plunged the world into inexorable sin and death. And lest we boast in ourselves, assuming we would have done much better, we should remember that we would have done *the very same thing*. Humanism is thus a full-on assault and campaign against God, his law order, and man's true purpose and calling. The healing of the nations can only come when we deal with this great predicament.

The Bible explains the core problem with mankind in this way when the serpent said to Adam and Eve: "For God knows that in the day you eat from it your eyes will be opened, and you will be like God, *knowing good and evil*" (Gen. 3:5, emphasis mine). The word 'knowing' should be understood to mean 'determining', as in, Adam and Eve, in their insurgency against God, would attempt to determine that which is righteous and that which is unrighteous, a task that solely belongs to God. It is this spirit of outlandish rebellion that marks humanism. This defiance, we should note, is the impulse of man to assert at every turn his superiority and sovereignty over and above God, worshiping and serving the created instead of the Creator (see Romans 1).

In chapter one I laid out the covenantal nature of the gospel of the Kingdom and God's subsequent relationship with the created order (man included). Since the goal of this book is to equip and educate toward the goal of healing the nations, it is important to know how this covenantal relationship works itself out in the world. Our current pharmaceutical cabal/unpleasantry derives much of its beliefs from humanist presuppositions, as we'll see shortly. Nevertheless, we need to note that the serpent's temptation of Adam and Eve was a *counterfeit* covenant with counterfeit terms and conditions. It was a false gospel preached to the first couple, and it is a false gospel that permeates the medical world today. Using covenant theology, we can ascertain the false narratives and presuppositions and combat them.

HUMANISM'S COVENANT

Throughout the Bible we find that the structure of God's covenant has five components, and the acronym spells out the Greek word for 'God': *THEOS*. They are: 1) Transcendence—who's in charge? Who is the ultimate authority? 2) Hierarchy—to whom do I report? 3) Ethics—what are the rules and parameters of the relationship? 4) Oaths—what happens when I obey? When I disobey? 5) Succession—what are the future plans and purposes of this relationship? What can we expect the future to look like?

Every counterfeit covenant will have these same elements (Satan is the great plagiarizer because he is unable to be creative like God) and for the humanist who rejects God's ethical parameters it looks like this:

1. **Transcendence**: Casting God aside, man is ultimately in charge of his own existence, and thus he is the ultimate authority. Since he is an evolutionary creature—molecules and matter in motion—he gets to determine his own survival and meaning. In the humanist formulation of the world, God does not have original ownership of the created order: man has inherited it from the primordial goo of naturalism. Man is thus the sovereign—*it could be no other way.*

2. **Hierarchy**: Man reports only to himself. He is not subordinate to God's authority, and as a result, he is not predisposed to God's demands. Man rules over the creation and asserts himself as the author and finisher of creation. He represents himself and therefore must control the natural world however he sees fit; it is simply his evolutionary impulse to control and manipulate others. (You can see why vaccine mandates come into play!)

3. **Ethics**: With man as central the rules and parameters of his being are therefore subjective and relative. In order to enforce his will, man must re-create the Tower of Babel (the all-seeing, all-knowing Orwellian State) and collectively demand subservience from those beneath him. When it comes to that which is right and wrong, the biblical/ethical model will not suffice. It is not what is right that matters, for this presupposes a transcendent standard, but that which is expedient takes primacy. And that which is expedient will only come about through power and coercion. Ethics become situational, pragmatic, and totalitarian.

4. **Oaths**: As it pertains to the implications of his newfound ethical worldview, man will only make an oath to himself, and certainly not to God. Man only answers to man and the repercussions for violating this covenantal oath

are purely subjective in nature. Man determines his own will and his own consequences. When the humanist is able to exert his power and authority, he will do so holding others to a different standard he himself cannot attain.

5. **Succession**: The future of this worldview is entirely political and self-serving. Being a law unto himself, man sees his word as being salvation. It is salvation by man's law, a works-based salvation. The future looks like the unceasing accumulation of power and control over other men. Liberty is a figment of the past; the State—man's incarnational god—is now the sovereign sustainer and helper. The future is evolutionary progress into the unknown. It is a blind progressivism with the desired result of more and more power.

WORLDVIEWS AT ODDS

A sad reality is that many unwitting Christians believe and defend some of these humanist concepts. They go on about Christians not being involved in such 'unspiritual' pursuits like medicine, politics, and vaccination. They remove themselves from these discussions because, so they believe, God does not have anything to say about them. It has been said that humanists believe in history but not God, while Christians believe in God but not history. These two worldviews could not be further apart. There is no reconciling them. There is no peace between them. They are at war with each other because both are irreconcilably starting from two different presuppositions. Christianity starts with God and his authority. Humanism starts with man and his self-proclaimed authority. Everything that flows from these foundational principles grows further and further apart, the result being endless conflict and frustration.

Yet the problem remains: Christians ought to believe in God *and* believe in history, for God is the author and orchestrator of history. He is the creator *and* the sustainer. He has proven himself to be concerned with history for He *entered* history in the Person and work of Jesus Christ. It is God's plan for the knowledge of Himself to cover the earth as the waters cover the sea (Hab. 2:14). But we don't always believe this, do we?

Humanists reject God and believe that history is the inevitable self-expression of man's self-determined, creative will. This 'you do you' religion has taken central stage in our colleges and universities because it believes and acts in and for history. As a result, humanism is an advancing ideology that has crushed the Christian West. The reason it has crushed the Christian West is because the Christian West *let it happen*. While Christians were focusing on their multi-billion-dollar buildings and programs, the pharmaceutical industry contended for culture by taking control, squashing (as we'll see in the coming chapters) any decentralized efforts at medicine and healthcare. Again, they did not just *take* the wheel, we jumped out of the car!

The quicker we can acknowledge that these worldviews are utterly and entirely opposed to one another, and the quicker we can repent (turn away by changing our minds) from handing the world over to the dominion and rule man, the quicker we can see liberty and prosperity thrive in the world. This will require a whole lot from Christians. It will require us to stop believing the myth of neutrality. There is no neutrality: either we are *with* Christ, or we are *against* Christ (Matt. 12:30). We live in God's covenant world which means there is only that which aligns with God, and that which has deviated from God. Nothing is neutral: everything is covenantal. Allopathic medicine, vaccination, glyphosate—all of it matters and either it aligns with God's law word, or it is opposed to God's law word. Christians who get this principle of 'no neutrality' down are Christians who are well-equipped to win the battle against humanism.

We also need to see the comprehensive gospel as outlined in chapter one as being a *global vision for healing*, which is the point of this book. No longer can we let the United Nations dictate to poorer countries things like abortion and homosexuality, especially when they dangle the almighty American dollar in front of them. Humanism is not going to go away until it is conquered with the gospel of the Kingdom. And humanism will go on completely unchallenged and unaffected by this gospel so long as Christians remain recluses, only coming out every four years for a presidential election. So, dear Christian, sound the alarm—we must wake up. Pastors must preach this, and churches must do something about it. However, there are more components to this problem that we need to keep in mind, especially considering the fact that our strategies and tactics are not the same as the humanist.

REFORMATION VS. ENLIGHTENMENT

For 500 years now, the West has been in constant flux due to the war between Christianity and humanism. When the Reformation spread across Western Europe, cultural renewal and revival took place. Men and women had a renewed vision and purpose for life. Thanks to the labors of Martin Luther, John Calvin, and Pierre Viret (to name only three), the liberty and freedom of the gospel saturated the land. Work and vocation now had a fresh purpose. The priesthood of all believers was hastily established and affirmed. The right and duty of private judgment was re-asserted with confidence. The centralized oligarchy of the Roman Catholic Church had received a severe blow as the Church was finally unleashed to serve the Kingdom and *not itself* nor its gatekeepers. *Protestantism started contending for culture.*

Even though the West was flourishing thanks to the gospel of the Kingdom, it was not without opposition. The Enlightenment, along with the Renaissance, spread just as quickly as men and women began to assert the centrality of man in their everyday lives. The Renaissance (15th & 16th centuries) was a revival of art and humanities, the Enlightenment (17th century) was more a scientific revolution. The former had more to do with literature and rediscovery of classical philosophy; the latter was about industrialization, rationality, and scientific methodology. Both were contenders for culture, and both were not without serious problems.

It was the French philosopher René Descartes (1596–1650), whose famous quip, *Cogito, ergo sum*, set the world on fire. The phrase is translated 'I think, therefore, I am' and it became the hallmark ideology for Enlightenment philosophy. Descartes's point was to establish a foundation for knowledge predicated on his ability to think and reason. The fact that man is able to think about and doubt his existence *proves* his existence. Why would he need God? While certainly other Enlightenment philosophers had their contributions, Descartes stands out among the giants.

When Adam and Eve sinned in the garden, their *thinking* became corrupted. Sure, they incurred the promise of physical death, and their emotion life was just as polluted. But we cannot forget that their *mind* was tainted, too. Contrary to the Enlightenment's elevation of man's reason—the belief that man's mind is ethically pure and neutral, untouched by sin and depravity—the Bible declares that the whole of man's being was poisoned by sin, *including* his thoughts. (Man's reason and thought processes did not go unscathed by our sin against God. This is why, at its root, the Enlightenment is philosophically untenable.)

One thing that Jesus died for was man's wrong thinking. Christ redeems your soul, no doubt, but He also redeems man's faulty thinking and reasoning. We are all made in the image of God and part of our image-bearing responsibility is our reflection of God in our thinking. We are *whole* beings and bodies: mind, soul, heart, and flesh. We think, we feel, and as a result of God's creative handiwork, we *are*. We *exist*. And we exist because God exists—the entirety of our being rests on Him. We were created to create, produced to produce, caused in order to cause. God thinks, we think. God feels, we feel. This is basic to Christian theology, which stands in sharp contrast to non-Christian theology.

Central to Cartesian philosophy are the following two assumptions: 1) Truth is self-existent, and thus it exists without any relationship to God. Humanists call these 'brute' facts. In other words, truth is not necessarily something that relies on God for its existence. 2) Our being, what we call 'ontology,' is derived, not necessarily from God, but from the fact that man *is* Reason. Permit me a moment to explain.

Because man 'thinks,' and his thinking has to be true otherwise we are delving into the realm of the absurd, man thus 'is.' Some sympathetic humanists would say that a god is somewhat important to this process; others would suggest that it is not. The underlying problem with Rationalism is the belief that our thinking is somehow independent of God. If sinful man can rid himself of accountability to God, he is thus free to think and free to explore whatever he wants. This type of reasoning has infiltrated the minds of many here in the West, and it is metastasizing all over the world. If man's reason is supreme, then man's thinking is free, and as a result his existence is free, free from any responsibility towards the Creator God.

In contrast to this rather dreadful position, the Bible presents something altogether contradictory to this philosophy. The Bible offers us a sharp distinction between the Creator God and created men (Rom. 1:18-32). It is not as though we are free to create our own existence, elevating our minds and wills above the created order. We are not free nor permitted to do so. Our minds are given to us by God in order to think God's thoughts after Him. The rebellious mind wants to declare autonomy—he wants to be a law unto himself (Gen. 3:5). The sanctified, holy mind wants to declare theonomy—he wants to be obedient to the law of God his Maker. This is the Christian theory of knowledge: knowing and being both presuppose the Creator and our accountability to Him in all things. As such, our tactics when dealing with humanism must be informed by these presuppositions.

POWER RELIGION VS. DOMINION RELIGION

There is one more paradigm I would like us to consider before we move on and it has everything to do with how these rival religions do battle in history. In chapter three we analyzed history and how we got in to the medical mess we are in; however, it is pertinent that we deal with these clashing strategies in order to better understand the mess.

Like Christianity, humanism as a doctrine is impractical unless it has a coherent blueprint for social action and order. Ideas have consequences and unfortunately it is we Christians who do not always see it this way. Humanism works with one central premise: the acquisition and maintenance of power. Since humanism works with the assumption of sovereignty of man over against the sovereignty of God, it can only attempt to accumulate and consolidate power in a centralized fashion. This worldview balks at the idea of serving the living God so it can only serve itself. Seeing that man is the product of evolutionary thought, why wouldn't he do what he can to advance his own agenda? Humanism is a religion because religion is simply faith and belief in a set of fixed presuppositions: faith in man, and belief in man's superiority.

In a manner of speaking, humanism is the inversion of the dominion covenant. Instead of being lawfully subordinate to God and His plans for the world, man serves only himself and exercises not a religion of servanthood dominion, but self-serving *domination*. A centralized power and control in the form of the State arises for the purpose of exerting man's own will. This is the power religion.

What makes Christianity distinguishable from this perversion of man's existence is God's law word. Christians do not live for themselves: they live to serve and worship God. As they serve God, they accomplish God's wishes for the world: *the cultivation of every area of life—including health—in order to advance human productivity and flourishing, all of it in service to God.* Economics plays an important role, too. When Christians and nations are faithful to God, exercising proper dominion through service and righteousness, God blesses and makes them fruitful, but only to the degree they align with biblical law. When cultures throw God into their own subjective trash can, God brings curses, stifling their productivity and unholy subjugation.

Power religionists force their will on others. Dominion religionists serve others, do what is right, and trust God in the process. Power religionists lie, cheat, and steal in order to get ahead and capture more and more power. Dominion religionists tell the truth, always share with others, and remain obedient stewards of what God has already given. Power religionists are secretive, hiding and obfuscating the vaccine ingredients so unsuspecting customers won't catch on. Dominion religionists walk in the light as h=He is in the light (1 John 1:7), men and women of integrity and entirely honest. As you can see, there is stark contrast between these worldviews. If the nations are to be healed, they are going to need to know and apply these principles.

CULTURE OF DEATH

The humanists have offered up nothing good for the world. Humanism's rotten fruit has resulted in Communism's bloody twentieth century. From Stalin to Hitler to Mao, the human lust for power and control knows no boundaries. A rejection of God Who is life will only incur death and destruction. Love your neighbor as yourself? That doctrine will not suffice. Love God and serve Him only? Not when you can do things your way. This constant impulse to rebellion and cosmic insurrection will only and always produce *death*. You cannot reject the Giver of life and expect life to be the resultant outcome. It does not work this way. It never works this way.

When it comes to how humanism works itself out in a culture of death, there are two main religious tactics involved. No movement or philosophy or cause in society can make progress and survive for the long haul without an identifiable philosophy of life and religious presupposition being embraced by its shareholders and foisted on its enemies. These are two of those main ideologies being foisted on us today, the first being *alchemy*.

Alchemy in a traditional sense refers to the medieval chemists whose experiments in utilizing gold and other materials to achieve health and wellness turned up void. In my definition, I am referring to the pharmaceutical industry's attempt at taking a witch's brew of adjuvants and trying to pretend as though injecting it into one's muscle tissue and blood stream will produce a positive outcome. If man is going to escape living in God's world, he is either going to have to kill himself or transcend himself. He has to become a new creation, and the way this is accomplished is through power and chemistry, an unholy union with colossal ramifications.

If the humanist is to transcend himself, he has to abolish time, reach a higher consciousness, and escape finitude. He must control the masses through statist interventionism. Whether it is the vehicle of government schools, infanticide, or a vaccine program, all of it falls underneath this draconian paradigm. Alchemy is the esoteric science of the religion of Gnosticism, and alchemists are what honest, self-conscious vaccines manufacturers should call themselves. To repeat: humanism in general will lead to a two-pronged strategy in order to imposes its will. Alchemy is the science; Gnosticism is the religion.

Gnosticism is an old religion dating back to the first and second centuries. Its meaning refers to 'secret spiritual knowledge' which is a means for control and power. In its early context it was a cult of self-proclaimed Christians who emphasized secret knowledge over the orthodox teaching of the Church. Gnostics never deal in terms of ethics; they do not affirm the concepts of sin and transgression and moral dysfunction. Instead, Gnostics speak of ignorance, the ultimate sin. Only when one obtains this secret knowledge can one be considered in the upper echelon of importance.

These two ideologies, alchemy and Gnosticism, are both deployed in the medical industry of our day. Case in point: scientific investigation. Science should not be a secret endeavor by the elite, government-controlled, and government-protected so-called 'experts.' It must be a publicly disclosed process[127] whereby there

---

127 Again, where is the double blind, placebo-controlled testing comparing vaccinated vs. unvaccinated patients, which would explain vaccine efficacy and safety?

is a division of labor, open knowledge with carefully documented data (there should be no government-protected exemptions on the disclosure of information and the responsibility for its contents), using repeatable experimentation, and basic consumer protection laws which govern injury to others. Human life should be of such a value as to exhaust all study, testing, and prospective solutions before administering medicine, *especially* vaccines.

Modern science came to the world because of the Reformation in Europe, not because of the Enlightenment. The only thing the Enlightenment has contributed to science is the attempted confiscation of science for the purposes of humanism: more power, secrecy, and control. Humanists took the presuppositions of the Enlightenment, married them to alchemy and Gnosticism, all for the purpose of controlling the material world with an eye toward totalitarian control.

What has it given us? Womb to tomb medicinal tyranny. If the humanist, allopathic industry cannot abort you, they'll give you autoimmune complications by repeatedly vaccinating you. If that doesn't work, they will get you on a statin as soon as possible (after all, heart disease can be a problem in your 30's). What's next? Booster shots for adults. More newly developed medicine with a million other side effects. Thus, the results of the humanist worldview.

CONCLUSION

Humanism is not just a philosophy: it is a religion. It is not just a religion, however: it is an ethical deviation from God's covenant standard. Due to its inescapable presuppositions, humanism flaunts itself as freedom but has sealed its fate. Its high-handed rebellion promises to have a far better program for human flourishing, but it only results in more disease, more cancer, more death. As a counterfeit covenant model, humanism hijacks the glory of God, desiring the glory of man to be worshiped and acknowledged in the world. This ancient, rival religion has offered the world a totalitarian nightmare. Power religion at its core is fundamentally at odds with the Christian gospel of peace, righteousness, and human longevity. It thrives on secrecy and mysticism.

The Christian answer to healing the nations looks nothing like the humanist vision. The kingdom of Jesus Christ is self-giving, not self-seeking. The kingdom that Christ came to establish is not about secrecy but walking in the light. It is the only true answer to the world's problems, including the problems we face pertaining to health and vitality. In a manner of speaking, this is a gospel issue: hence this book.

About the Author

Rev. Dr. Jason Garwood has spent his career seeking to both understand and apply the Biblical worldview to every single area of life. His aim is to help pastors and churches to be better equipped to engage in the Great Commission by teaching Christians how to find their individual purpose in the Kingdom of God and learn how to identify and respond to cultural idols.

He is currently the teaching pastor at Cross & Crown Church in Northern Virginia:
- Cross & Crown was planted in 2017 with a vision and mission to equip men, women, and children to press the crown rights of King Jesus into every area of life;
- Cross & Crown is a house-church movement seeking to establish other house churches across the world; and
- Cross & Crown is laboring to promote liberty and justice by local activism and involvement in the community.

He is a writer and activist:
- Jason is the author of several books, including *Reconstructing the Heart, Have Yourself An Eschatological Christ,* and *The Politics of Humanism;*
- He has written articles for various outlets and blogs at jasongarwood.com; and
- He has preached and lectured internationally on a variety

- of subjects, exposing the underling errors and problems with anti-biblical worldviews such as: government education, the drug war, the police state, humanist philosophy, and vaccines;
- You can find him at college campuses, high schools, and political meetings seeding the gospel of the Kingdom of Jesus Christ.

Most importantly, Jason is a devoted husband and father:
- He has been married to his wife, Mary, for 14 years;
- They have three children;
- He makes his home in Warrenton, Virginia.

CPSIA information can be obtained
at www.ICGtesting.com
Printed in the USA
BVHW041859251020
591783BV00024B/339